THE SILVER-B ARITHMETICS

COMPLETE BOOK

BY

GEORGE MORRIS PHILIPS, LL.D.

PRINCIPAL, WEST CHESTER, PA., STATE NORMAL SCHOOL; FORMERLY
PROFESSOR OF MATHEMATICS, BUCKNELL UNIVERSITY

AND

ROBERT F. ANDERSON, Sc.D.

PROFESSOR OF MATHEMATICS, WEST CHESTER, PA.,
STATE NORMAL SCHOOL

SILVER, BURDETT AND COMPANY

BOSTON   NEW YORK   CHICAGO

THE SILVER-BURDETT ARITHMETICS (Annotated) Selected Exercises

HP Prime Guide THE SILVER-BURDETT ARITHMETICS (Annotated) Selected Exercises
By LARRY SCHROEDER, MS Mathematics
Formerly Professor of Mathematics, Carl Sandburg College
Author Cengage Learning® and Computer Learning service

Published by
Computer Learning Service
1013 Woodbine Circle
Galesburg, IL 61401-2358
ComputerLearningService.com

Version 1.0.1

ISBN: 978-0-915573-01-1

In the *HP Prime Guide THE SILVER-BURDETT ARITHMETICS (Annotated) Selected Exercises* we parallel the content in the section and topics presented in our OneNote's *Basic Math* notebook. All web-based links shown in this publication are active in our *Basic Math* notebook. A link to our *Basic Math* notebook can be found on the home page of our *Prime Academy | Learning Center*.

OneNote's *Basic Math* notebook is a web based generic guide written to help HP Prime Calculator users learn how to use the calculator or software emulators to do fundamental arithmetic skills. The *HP Prime Guide THE SILVER-BURDETT ARITHMETICS (Annotated) Selected Exercises* is *THE SILVER-BURDETT ARITHMETICS* specific version with accompanying exercises and answers for that topic's content taken from *THE SILVER-BURDETT ARITHMETICS*.

Dedication

To my wife and children for their love and support.

CONTENTS

Terms of Use

By using *HP Prime Guide THE SILVER-BURDETT ARITHMETICS (Annotated) Selected Exercises* in any manner, you agree to all of the terms and conditions contained herein.

Trademarks: Cengage Learning ®, Thomson Learning™, WebTutor™ Brooks/Cole are registered trademarks of Cengage Learning Inc. HP Inc. has rights in the registered trademark HP, as well as its other registered and unregistered trademarks. T3™, Teachers Teaching with Technology™, TI-Nspire™, and TI-Navigator™ are registered trademarks of Texas Instruments Inc. iPhone ®, iPad ®, iPod ®, and Mac ® are registered trademarks of Apple Inc. All other trademarks are the property of their respective owners. Any usage of these terms anywhere throughout this book is done so simply as part of a description of the product. This book is in no way affiliated with or endorsed by Cengage Learning, HP, Texas Instruments, Apple or any other product or vendor mentioned in this book.

LIMIT OF LIABILITY/DISCLAIMER OF WARRANTY: THE PUBLISHER AND THE AUTHOR MAKE NO REPRESENTATIONS OR WATTANTIES WITH RESPECT TO THE ACCURACY OR COMPLETENESS OF THE CONTENTS OF THIS WORK AND SPECIFICALLY DISCLAIM ALL WARRANTIES, INCLUDING WITHOUT LIMITATION WARRANTIES OF FITNESS FOR A PARTICULAR PURPOSE. NO WARRANTIES MAY BE CREATED OR EXTENDED BT SALES MATERIALS. THE ADVICE AND STRATEGIES CONTAINED HEREN MAY NOT BE SUITABLE FOR EVERY SITUATION. THIS WORK IS SOLD WITH THE UNDERSTANDING THAT THE PUBLISHER IS NOT ENGAGED IN RENDERING LEGAL, ACCOUNTING, OR OTHER PROFESSIONAL SERVICES. IF PROFESSIONAL ASSISTANCED IS REQUIRED, THE SERVICES OF A COMPETENT PROFESSIONAL PERSON SHOULD BE SOUGHT. NEITHER THE PUBLISHER NOR THE AUTHOR SHALL BE LIABLE FOR DAMAGES, ARISING HEREFROM, THE FACT THAT AN ORGANIZATION OR WEBSITE IS REFERRED TO IN THIS WORK AS A A CITATION AND/OR A POTIENTIAL SOURCE OF FURTHER INFORMATION DOES NOT MEAN THAT THE AUTHOR OR THE PUBLISHER ENDORSES THE INOFRMATION THE ORGANIZATION OR WEBSITE MAY PROVIDE OR RECOMMENDATIONS IT MAY MAKE FURTHER, READER SHOULD BE AWARE THAT INTERNET WEBSITES LISTED IN THIS WORK MY HAVE CHANGED OR DISAPPEARED BETWEEN WHEN THIS WORK WAS WRITTEN AND WHEN IT IS READ.

PREFACE

I wish to thank the two authors George Morris Philips and Robert F Anderson, now deceased, for their early twentieth century work producing arithmetic books that introduced the subject to grammar school students or served as a review for many high school students that found a review of arithmetic profitable. I need to give thanks to the passing of time and being brought up in my grandmother's house. Their work, *The Silver-Burdett Arithmetics*, a four-book series has survived long enough for the copyrights to expire, the books to enter the public domain, and Google and Internet Archive to scan and preserve them. In an old pie chest, I got my hands on my aunt's, Rachel Schwartz Fouts, copy of *The Silver-Burdett Arithmetic, Complete Book* used by her in grammar school. My Aunt's book started me on this adventure.

For users of this annotated book, there is a digital copy of my Aunt's book that was preserved for generations on a library shelf at Harvard University Library before it was carefully scanned by Google as part of a project to make the world's books discoverable online. The scanned copy is of the book that was a Gift of The People of United States Through the Victory Book Campaign, to the Armed Forces and Merchant Marine, Normal Training School, New Haven, Conn. Hopefully, through Basic Math's OneNote's notebook we have brought it and the complete scanned *The Silver-Burdett Arithmetic* series, grades 1-8, into the modern era.

This annotated book is based on a limited structure that parallels the books in *The Silver-Burdett Arithmetic* series and their break down of topics used in early Twentieth century grammar schools. The annotated book reviews essential arithmetic skills and introduce HP Prime calculator's usefulness in mastering those skills. You can use any of Google's digital PDFs or Internet Archive digital sliders links listed in this section Resources' page to complement your current online, textbook, or handout's presentations and assignments. We have included for a topic's content specific related drill and practice exercises. The included drill and practice exercises allow you to practice and turn your HP Prime calculator into a valuable resource and learning tool.

Resources

CLS HP Prime Academy

    Prime Academy | Learning Center - website

    Generalities (settings and examples) HP Prime calculator

    Academy | HP Prime Table of Contents using Video links (fast internet connection advised)

YouTube

    HP PRIME 01 - Introduction and Set up

    Change HP Prime Screen Time

Forum

    HP Prime Code Snippets and Relative Help for Carbajo's Xcas YouTube Videos

Getting Started

The HP Prime Calculator is two calculators in one. First calculator is the Home View calculator. The [Home] View calculator is used in most of the tutorial. A second CAS calculator is available. The Computer Algebra System View [CAS] calculator is used for exact calculations that are mainly used in Algebra thru Post Calculus courses and their applications. Please note that a word in []s means to press that key on the HP Prime Calculator. Resources for the section's page and its subpage(s) are given as a subpage of that section.

This tutorial is a collection of basic math examples with explanations. A review of these examples and accompanying explanations will allow you to have success with courses or work requiring these skills. The tutorial is also useful for today's elementary and middle school learners acquiring these skills.

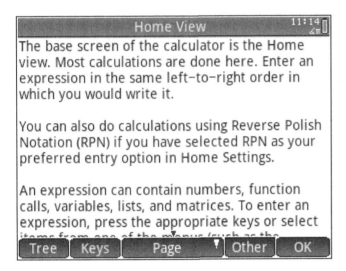

[Home] [Help]. Home View's help is displayed. Notice White shaded down arrow shown on soft Page key.

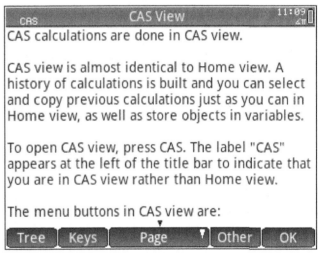

[CAS] [Help]. CAS View's help is displayed. [Esc] or soft key [OK] returns us to the current command line.

The Prime's built-in [Help] feature is a powerful tool. Turn the Prime on. Press [Home] [Help] keys and then soft key [OK] to close. Follow by the [CAS] [Help] keys. Home View - the first paragraph is the only paragraph that is applicable to the Basic Math tutorial; CAS View - the first three paragraphs are applicable to the tutorial. From time to time, we will use a HP Prime command that comes from the [Toolbox] key, soft key [Catlg] or soft key [CAS]. Use the Prime's [Help] system to display the command's features and sample examples.

HP Prime Guide

THE SILVER-BURDETT ARITHMETICS (Annotated) Selected Exercises

1

Whole Numbers

"It is India that gave us the ingenious method of expressing all numbers by means of ten symbols, each symbol receiving a value of position ... and we shall appreciate the grandeur of the achievement the more when we remember that it escaped the genius of Archimedes and Apollonius, two of the greatest men produced by antiquity."
~ Pierre Simon Laplace

Place Value – Addition

Subtraction

Multiplication

Division

Factors and Divisors (gcd)

Multiples (lcm)

Supplements

Place Value - Addition

Friday, December 10, 2021   4:59 PM

Place Value - How the Prime's Home View handles numbers. Prime settings determine the output displayed.

Hundred Billions	Ten Billions	Billions	Hundred Millions	Ten Millions	Millions	Hundred Thousands	Ten Thousands	Thousands	Hundreds	Tens	Ones	Tenths	Hundredths	Thousandths	Ten Thousandths	Hundred Thousandths
2	1	0	9	8	7	6	5	4	3	2	1	2	3	4	5	6

Two hundred ten billion, nine hundred eighty-seven million, six hundred fifty-four thousand, three hundred twenty-one, and twenty-three thousands, four hundred fifty-six hundred-thousandths

Function	03:19
210,987,654,321	210,987,654,321
1.75	1.75
1.750	1.750
1,750,000	1,750,000
1,750,000,000	1,750,000,000
1.75E12	1.75E12
1.75E9=1750000000	
Sto ▶ Save Load	

Use of E12 (trillion), E9 (billion), E6 (million) helpful in command line input. E3 (thousand) optional. Commas not allowed. Calculator displays only 12 digits. Use place value calculator to write decimal part in word form.

[Home] Entry of decimal number on left is truncated to twelve digits. Entry of 1.75, 1.75E3, 1.75E6, 1.75E9, 1.75 E12 are shown above. Example 1,750,000: [1.75] [EEX] [6] Note: Last entry displays 1 (True).

For Addition use Home View to display commas. Leave Prime set to default setting.

3754 + 2363
8471 + 8374
4732 + 3645
5663 + 2349

Function	18:16
3,754+2,363	6,117
8,471+8,374	16,845
4,732+3,645	8,377
5663+2349	
Sto ▶ Save Load	

Read aloud the word form of the calculator solution in the two screen's history area.

Read Aloud (word form)
8,595
56,197
375,836
8,932,420
640,476,353,571
175,920,473,819,411

Use Home View calculator.

[Home] Type in each entry as shown on left - be sure to leave out the commas. Following each entry by pressing [Enter].

Calculator keys - [Backspace] deletes keystroke - [Esc] clears command line - [Clear] after [Esc] erases History area.

9. Counting from the right, name the third place; the fourth; the sixth; the fifth; the seventh; the second; the eighth.

10. In the number 456, name the place that the 4 occupies; the 5; the 6.

11. In the number 86,475,239, what does the 86 represent? the 475? the 239?

Exercise 2

Read aloud each of these exercises:

1. 64,389,157

Thus, *sixty-four million three hundred eighty-nine thousand one hundred fifty-seven.*

2. 5619	3. 6038	4. 31,187
5. 67,802	6. 51,783	7. 432,107
8. 567,149	9. 733,924	10. 6,984,125
11. 3,907,534	12. 98,546,837	13. 87,631,052
14. 76,353,489	15. 563,819,306	16. 8,965,738,462

17. The average income of physicians in a certain state is $3907 a year, and the average expenses $3190.

18. The salary of the President of the United States is $75,000; the salary of the Vice President is $12,000.

19. The salary of the Governor of Illinois is $12,000.

20. The police force in New York City numbers more than 10,000.

14 WHOLE NUMBERS

2. A man bought a lot for $600, paid $65 to have it graded, $132 for paving, and $4250 to have a house built on it. What did his property cost him?

$600 = the cost of the lot.
$65 = the cost of the grading.
$132 = the cost of the paving.
$4250 = the cost of the house.
$5047 = the cost of the property.

Exercise 8

1. A man threshed his crop of grain; it consisted of 248 bu. of wheat, 678 bu. of oats, and 124 bu. of rye; how many bushels of grain were there in his crop?

2. Five loads of wheat weighed as follows: 3256 lb., 3478 lb., 3981 lb., 2108 lb., and 3456 lb.; how many pounds were there in the five loads?

3. A farmer's barn cost him as follows: for lumber $476; for masons' work $148; for hardware $62; for painting $85; and for grading $12; what did the barn cost him?

4. Copy and add:

A dealer bought in one week:

675	chickens weighing	3275 lb.	for $493
375	turkeys weighing	3300 lb.	for $495
245	ducks weighing	980 lb.	for $ 98
He bought	fowls weighing	lb.	for $

ANSWERS

Book Two

PART I

Exercise 7, page 12

1. 567,574.	2. 856,360.	3. 1,043,136.	4. 4,341,485.	5. 2,940,781.
6. 1,352,077.	7. 2,210,068.	8. 1,089,857.	9. 2,084,178.	10. 2,008,520.
11. 3,241,763.	12. 3,082,272.	13. 406,702.	14. 320,148.	15. 41,619,570.

Exercise 8, page 14

1. 1050.	2. 16,279.	3. $783.	4. 1295 ; 7555 ; 1086.

Exercise 10, page 16

1. 1391.	2. 97.	3. 1087.	4. 3314.	5. 852.
6. 2549.	7. 3998.	8. 3722.	9. 1689.	10. 3769.
11. 19,885.	12. 14,206.	13. 18,379.	14. 26,387.	15. 18,881.
16. 30,548.	17. 38,378.	18. 23,348.	19. 19,689.	20. 38,812.
21. 388,159.	22. 279,849.	23. 2874.	24. 230,971.	25. 160,909.
26. 389,685.	27. 559,956.	28. 192,589.	29. 188,791.	30. 567,907.
31. 76,239.	32. 39,908.			

Exercise 11, page 18

1. $358.	2. $4581.	3. 2092.	4. $57.	5. $369.	6. 449 ; 300 ; 210.

Exercise 15, page 22

1. 93,612.	2. 123,410.	3. 229,704.	4. 276,792.
5. 195,020.	6. 275,307.	7. 380,700.	8. 422,518.
9. 344,280.	10. $10,947.42.	11. $14,066.25.	12. $13,770.
13. 382,761.	14. 472,236.	15. 292,815.	16. 420,992.
17. 397,020.	18. 462,480.	19. 602,905.	20. 667,320.
21. 617,234.	22. 2,565,052.	23. 4,410,880.	24. 5,334,252.
25. 10,325,788.	26. 17,590,960.	27. 31,331,030.	28. 25,299,051.
29. 30,440,904.	30. 34,207,824.	31. 48,875,080.	32. 50,965,470.
33. 50,490,570.	34. 59,173,125.	35. 61,149,960.	36. 77,986,190.

i

Subtraction

Wednesday, December 8, 2021   11:25 PM

For Subtraction use Home View to display commas. Leave Prime set to default setting.

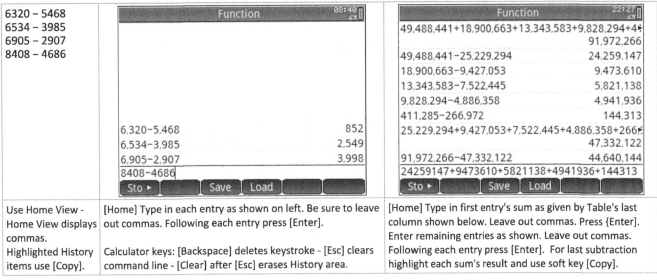

6320 – 5468		
6534 – 3985		
6905 – 2907		
8408 – 4686		

| Use Home View - Home View displays commas. Highlighted History items use [Copy]. | [Home] Type in each entry as shown on left. Be sure to leave out commas. Following each entry press [Enter]. Calculator keys: [Backspace] deletes keystroke - [Esc] clears command line - [Clear] after [Esc] erases History area. | [Home] Type in first entry's sum as given by Table's last column shown below. Leave out commas. Press {Enter}. Enter remaining entries as shown. Leave out commas. Following each entry press [Enter]. For last subtraction highlight each sum's result and use soft key [Copy]. |

In 1910 Census total population. Fill in the blank entries. See screen above. Categories from the 1910 Census

NATIVITY AND COLOR	MALES	FEMALES	TOTAL	MISSING ADDEND
Native White				How many females were born to foreign
Native Parents	25,229,294		49,488,441	parents?
Foreign Parents	9,427,053		18,900,663	9,427,053 + _____ = 18,900,663
Foreign White	7,522,445		13,343,583	
Negro	4,886,358		9,828,294	What was the total female population ?
All other	266,972		411,285	47,432,122+ _____ = 91,972,266 (multiple step problem)
TOTAL				

Missing addends values. Values are found in Prime entries 2-6 and 8 of History area of screen. Press [Enter] to total the Females' value copied from History into command line separated by [+]s. The result will be 44,640,144.

16   **WHOLE NUMBERS**

Give the results at sight:

9. 49 − 20.

Thus, say instantly, *29*.

10. 78 − 32.

Thus, think 78 minus 30 minus 2; say instantly, *46*.

11. 82 − 25.

Thus, think 82 minus 20 minus 5; say instantly, *57*.

12. 65 − 20	13. 86 − 30	14. 58 − 16
15. 96 − 42	16. 78 − 25	17. 97 − 56
18. 41 − 28	19. 52 − 48	20. 60 − 18
21. 54 − 36	22. 85 − 47	23. 91 − 26

Exercise 10

(Accuracy and Speed Test. Practice until you can subtract all examples in this exercise in less than 10 minutes. Check by adding the difference to the subtrahend to make the minuend.)

1. 3754 2363	2. 8471 8374	3. 4732 3645	4. 5663 2349
5. 6320 5468	6. 6534 3985	7. 6905 2907	8. 8408 4686
9. 7074 5385	10. 7136 3367	11. 32964 13079	12. 42580 28374
13. 78013 59634	14. 93486 67099	15. 97523 78642	16. 60413 29865

| 17. | 55463 | 18. | 76054 | 19. | 39064 | 20. | 87531 |
| | 17085 | | 52706 | | 19375 | | 48719 |

| 21. | 874312 | 22. | 520016 | 23. | 401435 | 24. | 751946 |
| | 486153 | | 240167 | | 398561 | | 520975 |

| 25. | 329648 | 26. | 420653 | 27. | 619862 | 28. | 367452 |
| | 168739 | | 30968 | | 59906 | | 174863 |

| 29. | 437109 | 30. | 617542 | 31. | 86146 | 32. | 48007 |
| | 248318 | | 49635 | | 9907 | | 8099 |

Problems

6. 1. There were 380,546 people living in Maryland in 1810 and 1,295,346 in 1910; what was the increase for the hundred years?

> 1,295,346 = the population of Maryland in 1910.
> 380,546 = the population of Maryland in 1810.
> ———————
> 914,800 = the increase in the 100 years.

2. The Mississippi River is 3160 miles long and the Arkansas 2170 miles long; what is their difference in length?

> 3160 mi. = the length of the Mississippi River.
> 2170 mi. = the length of the Arkansas River.
> ———————
> 990 mi. = the difference in length.

ANSWERS

Book Two

PART I

Exercise 7, page 12

1. 567,574.	2. 856,360.	3. 1,043,136.	4. 4,841,485.	5. 2,940,781.
6. 1,352,077.	7. 2,210,068.	8. 1,089,857.	9. 2,084,178.	10. 2,008,520.
11. 3,241,763.	12. 3,082,272.	13. 406,702.	14. 320,148.	15. 41,619,570.

Exercise 8, page 14

1. 1050.	2. 16,279.	3. $783.	4. 1295 ; 7555 ; 1086.

Exercise 10, page 16

1. 1391.	2. 97.	3. 1087.	4. 3314.	5. 852.
6. 2549.	7. 3998.	8. 3722.	9. 1689.	10. 3769.
11. 19,885.	12. 14,206.	13. 18,379.	14. 26,387.	15. 18,881.
16. 30,548.	17. 38,378.	18. 23,348.	19. 19,689.	20. 38,812.
21. 388,159.	22. 279,849.	23. 2874.	24. 230,971.	25. 160,909.
26. 389,685.	27. 559,956.	28. 192,589.	29. 188,791.	30. 567,907.
31. 76,239.	32. 39,908.			

Exercise 11, page 18

1. $358.	2. $4581.	3. 2092.	4. $57.	5. $369.	6. 449 ; 300 ; 210.

Exercise 15, page 22

1. 93,612.	2. 123,410.	3. 229,704.	4. 276,792.
5. 195,020.	6. 275,307.	7. 380,700.	8. 422,518.
9. 344,280.	10. $10,947.42.	11. $14,066.25.	12. $13,770.
13. 382,761.	14. 472,236.	15. 292,815.	16. 420,992.
17. 397,020.	18. 462,480.	19. 602,905.	20. 667,320.
21. 617,234.	22. 2,565,052.	23. 4,410,880.	24. 5,334,252.
25. 10,325,788.	26. 17,590,960.	27. 31,331,030.	28. 25,299,051.
29. 30,440,904.	30. 34,207,824.	31. 48,875,080.	32. 50,965,470.
33. 50,490,570.	34. 59,173,125.	35. 61,149,960.	36. 77,986,1ʁʊ.

i

Multiplication

Sunday, December 12, 2021   7:19 PM

Multiplication introduces the use of lists, {}s, and commands. Leave Prime set to default setting.

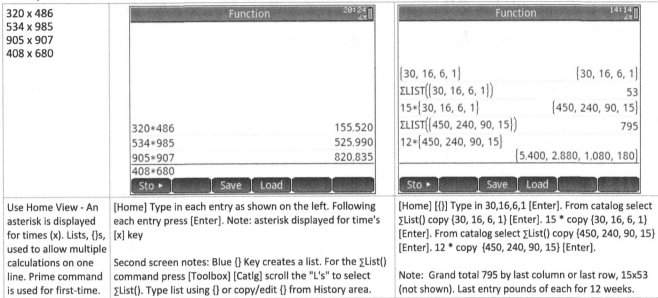

320 x 486 534 x 985 905 x 907 408 x 680	**Function** 20:24 320*486 155,520 534*985 525,990 905*907 820,835 408*680 Sto ▶ Save Load	**Function** 14:14 {30, 16, 6, 1} {30, 16, 6, 1} ΣLIST({30, 16, 6, 1}) 53 15*{30, 16, 6, 1} {450, 240, 90, 15} ΣLIST({450, 240, 90, 15}) 795 12*{450, 240, 90, 15} {5,400, 2,880, 1,080, 180} Sto ▶ Save Load
Use Home View - An asterisk is displayed for times (x). Lists, {}s, used to allow multiple calculations on one line. Prime command is used for first-time.	[Home] Type in each entry as shown on the left. Following each entry press [Enter]. Note: asterisk displayed for time's [x] key Second screen notes: Blue {} Key creates a list. For the ΣList() command press [Toolbox] [Catlg] scroll the "L's" to select ΣList(). Type list using {} or copy/edit {} from History area.	[Home] [{}] Type in 30,16,6,1 [Enter]. From catalog select ΣList() copy {30, 16, 6, 1} [Enter]. 15 * copy {30, 16, 6, 1} [Enter]. From catalog select ΣList() copy {450, 240, 90, 15} [Enter]. 12 * copy {450, 240, 90, 15} [Enter]. Note: Grand total 795 by last column or last row, 15x53 (not shown). Last entry pounds of each for 12 weeks.

Rations per day for feeding a cow is given in column 3. Table is for 15 cows. Fill in totals. See screen above. Note: scalar (number) times a list {} for TOTAL entries.

How many pounds of each of the food products given in the rations are required to keep 15 cows fed for 12 weeks? Hint: use lists {} for calculations. (5,400, 2,880, 1,080, 180)

COMPONENT	COWS	POUNDS PER COW	TOTAL
Corn silage	15	30	
Red clover hay	15	16	
Corn	15	6	
Cottonseed meal	15	1	
TOTAL	15		

22   **WHOLE NUMBERS**

31. 200×8 32. 300×6 33. 200×9

34. $24 \times \$2$ 35. $48 \times \$2$ 36. $32 \times \$4$

37. $46 \times \$3$ 38. $27 \times \$3$ 39. $21 \times \$4$

Multiplication of Any Number by a Number of Two Figures or More

12. Multiply 3582 by 346.

$$\begin{array}{r} 3582 \\ 346 \\ \hline 21492 \\ 14328 \\ 10746 \\ \hline 1239372 \end{array}$$

The multiplier is $300 + 40 + 6$.

$6 \times 3582 =$ what?   (1st partial product)

$40 \times 3582 =$ what?   (2d partial product)

$300 \times 3582 =$ what?   (3d partial product)

What does the 8 of the 2d partial product express?

In the form, what figure is omitted from the 2d partial product?

What does the 6 of the 3d partial product express?

In the form, what figures are omitted from the 3d partial product?

Special Forms

(A)	(B)	(C)	(D)
$75.25	3286	4586	7600
37	304	3009	270
526 75	13144	41274	532
2257 5	9858	13758	152
$2784.25	998944	13799274	2052000

Exercise 15

1. 348×269 2. 287×430 3. 408×563

4. 456×607 5. 398×490 6. 563×489

7. 675×564 8. 578×731 9. 570×604

10. $513 \times \$21.34$	11. $465 \times \$30.25$	12. $324 \times \$42.50$
13. 639×599	14. 667×708	15. 723×405
16. 704×598	17. 780×509	18. 820×564
19. 865×697	20. 996×670	21. 878×703
22. 569×4508	23. $640. \times 6892$	24. 753×7084
25. 4306×2398	26. 3097×5680	27. 4670×6709
28. 5073×4987	29. 6708×4538	30. 5007×6832
31. 8135×6008	32. 7830×6509	33. 6998×7215
34. 8305×7125	35. 7080×8637	36. 9065×8603

Problems

13. 1. A printing press that prints 295 copies of a paper in a minute will print how many copies in 9 minutes?

295 = the number of copies printed in 1 minute.

   9
———
2655 = the number of copies printed in 9 minutes.

2. Find the cost of 375 tons of coal at $6 a ton.

Suggestion. — $375 \times \$6 = 6 \times \$375$.

Exercise 16

1. At $175 an acre, what will a farm of 250 acres cost?

2. How much tuition is paid in a year by 900 students, if each pays $250?

3. How many pounds are there in 35 bales of cotton, each weighing 500 lb.?

ANSWERS

Book Two

PART I

Exercise 7, page 12

1. 567,574. **2.** 856,360. **3.** 1,043,136. **4.** 4,341,485. **5.** 2,940,781.
6. 1,352,077. **7.** 2,210,068. **8.** 1,089,857. **9.** 2,084,178. **10.** 2,008,520.
11. 3,241,763. **12.** 3,082,272. **13.** 406,702. **14.** 320,148. **15.** 41,619,570.

Exercise 8, page 14

1. 1050. **2.** 16,279. **3.** $783. **4.** 1295; 7555; 1086.

Exercise 10, page 16

1. 1391. **2.** 97. **3.** 1087. **4.** 3314. **5.** 852.
6. 2549. **7.** 3998. **8.** 3722. **9.** 1689. **10.** 3769.
11. 19,885. **12.** 14,206. **13.** 18,379. **14.** 26,387. **15.** 18,881.
16. 30,548. **17.** 38,378. **18.** 23,348. **19.** 19,689. **20.** 38,812.
21. 388,159. **22.** 279,849. **23.** 2874. **24.** 230,971. **25.** 160,909.
26. 389,685. **27.** 559,956. **28.** 192,589. **29.** 188,791. **30.** 567,907.
31. 76,239. **32.** 39,908.

Exercise 11, page 18

1. $358. **2.** $4581. **3.** 2092. **4.** $57. **5.** $369. **6.** 449; 300; 210.

Exercise 15, page 22

1. 93,612. **2.** 123,410. **3.** 229,704. **4.** 276,792.
5. 195,020. **6.** 275,307. **7.** 380,700. **8.** 422,518.
9. 344,280. **10.** $10,947.42. **11.** $14,066.25. **12.** $13,770.
13. 382,761. **14.** 472,236. **15.** 292,815. **16.** 420,992.
17. 397,020. **18.** 462,480. **19.** 602,905. **20.** 667,320.
21. 617,234. **22.** 2,565,052. **23.** 4,410,880. **24.** 5,334,252.
25. 10,325,788. **26.** 17,590,960. **27.** 31,331,030. **28.** 25,299,051.
29. 30,440,904. **30.** 34,207,824. **31.** 48,875,080. **32.** 50,965,470.
33. 50,490,570. **34.** 59,173,125. **35.** 61,149,960. **36.** 77,986,195.

i

Division

Thursday, December 9, 2021   10:48 AM

Division(÷) problems are transformed into fractions. Leave Prime set to default setting.

| No remainder
Divide
2176 ÷ 32
16555 ÷ 43

Remainder
Divide
5378 ÷ 89
7568 ÷ 1000 | Remainder Discussion (max 12 digits)
Prime History area [a b/c] toggles result
$\dfrac{5{,}378}{89} = 60.4269662921$

      Alternate Form: 60 R 38 use numerator
$\dfrac{7{,}568}{1000} = 7.568$

      Alternate Form: 7 R 568 use iquorem

Decimal – Improper Fraction - Mixed Numeral
Up to 12 digits - Exact - Exact uses a plus (+) sign

Alternate form: Quotient R Remainder | 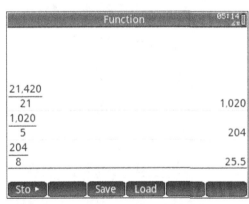 |
| Command line - Calculator displays a division problem as an improper fraction. Uses the [÷] key. Use command, iquorem, for remainder. | Remainders in mixed numeral form with a denominator the same as the divisor is the numerator of the fraction part (entry 3 in screen). The calculator will reduce the fraction in mixed numeral form (entry 4 in screen). In these cases use iquorem(dividend, divisor) for quotient and remainder (command line in screen). | [Home] Type in entries on the left. Use the [÷] key Use [a b/c] to toggle divisions with a remainder between decimal, improper fraction, and mixed numeral.

Using iquorem(768,1000) in the command line will return [7 568], 7 remainder 568. [Enter] is pressed. |

If 21 new packing plant workers working 8 hours a day, earn $21,420 in 5 days. How much does each worker earn per week? Earn per day? Earn per hour? Hint: make use of History's area soft key [Copy] ($1,020, $204, $25.50)

(Since they were new, they all receive the same pay per hour. Note that all the new workers worked 8 hours a day for the 5 day week.)

[Home} Type in divisions as shown. Use the [÷] key.

28   WHOLE NUMBERS

Special Form

Divide 627 by 200.

This shows the complete work: *In practice write only this:*

$200\overline{)627} = 200\overline{)600 + 27}$ $2\cancel{00}\overline{)6 \mid 27}$

$3 + \frac{27}{200}$ $3\frac{27}{200}$

Exercise 19

Divide:

1. 2176 by 32	2. 4462 by 46	3. 4984 by 56
4. 5378 by 89	5. 1005 by 67	6. 7569 by 87
7. 7560 by 35	8. 17,325 by 25	9. 16,555 by 43
10. 33,761 by 49	11. 65,142 by 77	12. 34,970 by 26
13. 142,196 by 38	14. 383,614 by 47	15. 182,790 by 45
16. 13,212 by 48	17. 20,145 by 56	18. 37,604 by 63
19. 48,325 by 95	20. 40,106 by 87	21. 41,001 by 97
22. 142,272 by 416	23. 111,616 by 218	24. 211,932 by 609
25. 39,552 by 309	26. 477,006 by 642	27. 586,704 by 816
28. 480,198 by 489	29. 34,968 by 215	30. 236,418 by 300

Problems

21. 1. If 45 beams of equal weight weigh 16,200 lb. how much does each beam weigh?

```
        360 lb. = the weight of each.
45)16200 lb. = the total weight.
   135
   270
   270
     0
```

2. A miller shipped 9800 lb. of flour in barrels; how many barrels did he ship if a barrel contains 196 lb.?

9800 lb. = the quantity of flour shipped.
196 lb. = the weight of each barrel.
50 = the number of barrels

196)9800
       980
       ___
          0

Exercise 20

1. 84 town lots are valued at $44,184. If the lots are of equal value, what is the value of each?

2. If 12 acres of land produce 288 bu. of wheat, how much is that to the acre?

3. A farmer sold his farm, consisting of 85 acres, for $5100; how much was that an acre?

4. A teamster hauled 1190 rails in 14 loads; how many was that to the load?

5. Wheat weighs 60 lb. to the bushel. A farmer's wheat crop weighed 10,600 lb. How many bushels had he and how many pounds over?

6. A clerk who saves $25 a month will require how many months to save enough to pay for a $4000 house?

7. A mail carrier, whose route covers 24 miles per day, covers 12,000 miles in how many days?

ANSWERS

Exercise 16, page 23

1. $43,750.   2. $225,000.   3. 17,500.   4. $1375.
5. 2,232,000 mi.   6. $78,000.   7. 6540 ft.   8. 1104 gal.

Exercise 19, page 28

1. 68.   2. 97.   3. 89.   4. 60; remainder 38.
5. 15.   6. 87.   7. 216.   8. 693.
9. 385.   10. 689.   11. 846.   12. 1345.
13. 3742.   14. 8162.   15. 4062.   16. 275; remainder 12.
17. 359; remainder 41.   18. 596; remainder 56.   19. 508; remainder 65.
20. 460; remainder 86.   21. 422; remainder 67.   22. 342.   23. 512.
24. 348.   25. 128.   26. 743.   27. 719.   28. 982.
29. 162; remainder 138.   30. 788; remainder 18.

Exercise 20, page 29

1. $526.   2. 24 bu.   3. $60.   4. 85.   5. 176; 40.   6. 160.
7. 500.   8. 803 lb.   9. 72 yr.   10. 8 yr.   11. 3945 lb.   12. 132.
13. 1760.   14. 60.

Exercise 21, page 30

2. 32,025,000.   3. CXVI; XCIV.   4. MDCL; MCDL.
5. 798; $534.68.   6. $1320.   7. $8220.   8. 1826.   9. $10.04.
10. $331.   11. 21,780   12. $975.   13. 2160.   14. 9346   15. 392.
16. 50.   17. 75¢.   18. $25.80.   19. 76 yr.
20. The latter by $9.   21. $16.50.   22. 987,960.   23. 10.
24. 10.   25. 12.   26. 40.   27. 62,500.   28. $60.75.
29. 1950 lb.   30. $114.96.   31. $14.64.   32. 1440.

Exercise 22, page 35

1. 5.   2. 15.   3. 18.   4. 6.   5. 35.   6. 20.
7. 31.   8. 1.   9. 12.   10. 120.   11. 26.   12. 122.
13. 401.   14. 1312.   15. 1007.

Exercise 23, page 37

12. 1, 2, 3, 5, 7, 11, 13, 17, 19.
13. 4, 6, 8, 9, 10, 12, 14, 15, 16, 18, 20, 21, 22, 24, 25, 26, 27, 28.
15. 2, 5.   16. 2, 2, 3.   17. 3, 5.   18. 2, 2, 5.   19. 5, 5.   20. 2, 3, 5.
21. 2, 2, 2, 2.   22. 2, 2, 3, 3.   23. 2, 2, 2, 2, 3.
24. 2, 5, 5.   25. 2, 3, 3, 3.   26. 2, 2, 3, 5.   27. 3, 3, 5.
28. 2, 2, 2, 5.   29. 2, 2, 2, 3.   30. 2, 2, 2, 2, 2.

Factors and Divisors (gcd)

Wednesday, December 15, 2021   4:02 AM

For commands ifactors, isprime, ifactor, and igcd press [Toolbox] - if necessary select soft key [Catlg] letter - press I (TAN key) and scroll. For gcd, same except press G (SIN key). Also available by soft key [CAS].

The **factors** of a number are such numbers as multiplied together will produce the number. Thus, the factors of 15 are 3 and 5. A number that has no other factors than itself and 1 is a **prime number** ; as, 5 = 5 x 1. A number composed of other factors than itself and 1 is a **composite number** ; as, 21 = 3 x 7.	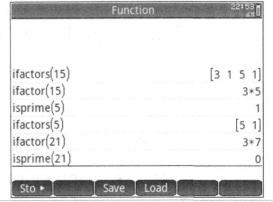
HP Prime Catalog contains commands used on this page. If you know the command it can be typed in the command line with opening and closing parenthesis.	See above directions to add commands to the command line - Ifactors second part for each prime is how many - isprime entry displays 1 (True), a display of 0 (False).

When all the factors of a number are prime numbers, they are called the **prime factors** of the number.
    Thus, in 12 = 2 x 2 x 3 - 2, 2, and 3 are the prime factors of 12.
 	
The product of all the common prime factors of two or more numbers is their **greatest common divisor**.
    Thus, the greatest common divisor of 90, 120, and 210 is 2 x 5 x 3
	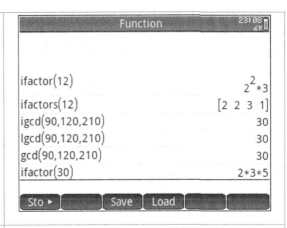

2	90	120	210	
5	45	60	105	Thus, 2, 5, and 3, are the common prime divisors of 90, 120, and 210. Therefore, 2 x 5 x 3 or 30 is greatest common divisor of 90, 120, and 210.
3	9	12	21	
	3	4	7	

See above directions to add the command to command line. Exponent(s) same factor more than once.

36 WHOLE NUMBERS

FACTORS AND DIVISORS

28. The **factors** of a number are such numbers as multiplied together will produce the number.

Thus, the factors of 15 are 3 and 5.

29. A number that has no other factor than itself and 1 is a **prime number**; as, $5 = 5 \times 1$.

30. A number composed of other factors than itself and 1 is a **composite number**; as, $15 = 5 \times 3$.

31. The same factor may be used more than once in forming a composite number. Each time it is so used it is considered a separate factor.

Thus, $36 = 2 \times 2 \times 3 \times 3$; here the factors of 36 are shown to be 2, 2, 3, and 3.

32. When all the factors of a number are prime numbers they are called the **prime factors** of the number.

Thus, in $12 = 2 \times 2 \times 3$, the prime factors of 12 are 2, 2, and 3.

Exercise 23

Name two factors that will produce

1. 6; 10; 15; 18. 2. 8; 9; 16; 25.
3. 14; 24; 21; 36. 4. 28; 52; 49; 50.
5. 56; 48; 63; 72. 6. 81; 54; 90; 110.

Name three factors that will produce

7. 12; 8; 27; 20. 8. 30; 28; 50; 42.

Tell which of the following numbers are prime:

9. 1; 2; 5; 8; 11; 14; 21.

10. 3; 6; 9; 12; 15; 18; 23.

11. 4; 7; 10; 13; 16; 20; 25.

12. Write all the prime numbers that are less than 20.

13. Write all the composite numbers that are less than 30.

Find the prime factors of:

14. 18   Thus, $18 = 2 \times 3 \times 3$.

15. 10	16. 12	17. 15	18. 20
19. 25	20. 30	21. 16	22. 36
23. 48	24. 50	25. 54	26. 60
27. 45	28. 40	29. 24	30. 32

33. A number that will divide a given number without a remainder is an **exact divisor**, or simply a **divisor**, of the given number.

Thus, 5 is a divisor of 10, but not of 11.

34. A divisor of each of two or more numbers is called a **common divisor** of them.

Thus, 5 is a common divisor of 10 and 20.

35. The greatest number that will divide each of two or more numbers is called their **greatest common divisor** (**g. c. d.**).

Thus, 5 is the greatest common divisor of 10, 15, and 20.

ii   '   **ANSWERS**

Exercise 16, page 23

1. $43,750.   2. $225,000.   3. 17,500.   4. $1375.
5. 2,232,000 mi.   6. $78,000.   7. 6540 ft.   8. 1104 gal.

Exercise 19, page 28

1. 68.   2. 97.   3. 89.   4. 60 ; remainder 38.
5. 15.   6. 87.   7. 216.   8. 693.
9. 385.   10. 689.   11. 846.   12. 1345.
13. 3742.   14. 8162.   15. 4062.   16. 275 ; remainder 12.
17. 359 ; remainder 41.   18. 596 ; remainder 56.   19. 508 ; remainder 65.
20. 460 ; remainder 86.   21. 422 ; remainder 67.   22. 342.   23. 512.
24. 348.   25. 128.   26. 743.   27. 719.   28. 982.
29. 162 ; remainder 138.   30. 788 ; remainder 18.

Exercise 20, page 29

1. $526.   2. 24 bu.   3. $60.   4. 85.   5. 176; 40.   6. 160.
7. 500.   8. 803 lb.   9. 72 yr.   10. 8 yr.   11. 3945 lb.   12. 132.
13. 1760.   14. 60.

Exercise 21, page 30

2. 32,025,000.   3. CXVI ; XCIV.   4. MDCL ; MCDL.
5. 798 ; $534.68.   6. $1320.   7. $8220.   8. 1826.   9. $10.04.
10. $331.   11. 21,780   12. $975.   13. 2160.   14. 9346   15. 392.
16. 50.   17. 75¢.   18. $25.80.   19. 76 yr.
20. The latter by $9.   21. $16.50.   22. 987,960.   23. 10.
24. 10.   25. 12.   26. 40.   27. 62,500.   28. $60.75.
29. 1950 lb.   30. $114.96.   31. $14.64.   32. 1440.

Exercise 22, page 35

1. 5.   2. 15.   3. 18.   4. 6.   5. 35.   6. 20.
7. 31.   8. 1.   9. 12.   10. 120.   11. 26.   12. 122.
13. 401.   14. 1312.   15. 1007.

Exercise 23, page 37

12. 1, 2, 3, 5, 7, 11, 13, 17, 19.
13. 4, 6, 8, 9, 10, 12, 14, 15, 16, 18, 20, 21, 22, 24, 25, 26, 27, 28.
15. 2, 5.   16. 2, 2, 3.   17. 3, 5.   18. 2, 2, 5.   19. 5, 5.   20. 2, 3, 5.
21. 2, 2, 2, 2.   22. 2, 2, 3, 3.   23. 2, 2, 2, 2, 3.
24. 2, 5, 5.   25. 2, 3, 3, 3.   26. 2, 2, 3, 5.   27. 3, 3, 5.
28. 2, 2, 2, 5.   29. 2, 2, 2, 3.   30. 2, 2, 2, 2, 2.

Multiples LCM

Wednesday, December 8, 2021   11:35 PM

For commands idivis and mat2list press [Toolbox] - if necessary select soft key [Catlg] letter - press I (TAN key) and scroll. For mat2list, same except press M (+/- key). Also available by soft key [CAS]. Blue {} (8 key) creates a list.

A number that a given number will exactly divide is called a **multiple** of the given number.
 	
    Thus, 6 is a multiple of 2 - since 2 will exactly divide 6.
    Screen's idivis(6) - 6 is a multiple of {1,2,3,6} - {1,2,3,6} exactly divides 6
 	
Note: When copying a Matrix [] from the History to the command edit line +/- (s) are added. The +/- (s) with the [+] and [-] keys being used to add or delete rows and columns within the command edit line. Ignore the +/- when the dimension stays the same.
 	
When dealing with matrix []'s multiplication and division rules are simpler for lists {}. Thus, the use of mat2list command. The Error message demonstrates that division of a number by a list {} works but not for a matrix [].
	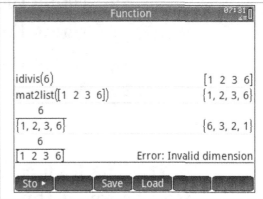

HP Prime Catalog contains commands used on this page. If you know the command it can be typed in the command line with opening and closing parenthesis.	See above directions to add the command to the command line. Matrix []s uses row by columns. A converted row matrix looks similar to a list {}.

A number that each of two or more numbers will exactly divide is called a **common multiple** of them.
 	
    Thus, 12 is a common multiple of 2 and 3, since 2 and 3 will each exactly divide 12.
 	
The least number that each of two or more numbers will exactly divide is called their **least common multiple**.
 	
    Thus, 6 is the least common multiple of 2 and 3, since 6 is the least number that 2 and 3 will exactly divide.
	Function 08:22
	ifactor(12) 2^2*3
	  12
	{2, 3} {6, 4}
	lcm(2,3) 6
	ifactors({60, 90})
	    {[2 2 3 1 5 1], [2 1 3 2 5 1]}
	2^2*3^2*5 180
	lcm(60,90) 180
	Sto ▸ Save Load

$60 = 2 \, x \, 2 \, x \, 3 \, x \, 5$ $90 = 2 \, x \, 3 \, x \, 5 \, x \, 3$ The least common multiple of 60 and 90 must contain the prime factors 2, 2, 3, and 5 in order to contain 60; it must contain an additional 3 in order to contain 90. Therefore $2 \, x \, 2 \, x \, 3 \, x \, 5 \, x \, 3 = 180$	See above directions to add the command to command line. Ifactors second part for each prime is how many. Entry 5 type - exponent(s) same factor more than once.

31. Name the numbers that are divisible by 2.

32. Name the numbers that are divisible by 5.

33. Name the numbers that are divisible by 4.

34. Name the numbers that are divisible by 3.

35. Name the numbers that are divisible by 9.

Multiples

11. The least common multiple of two or more numbers may be found thus:

$$60 = 2 \times 2 \times 3 \times 5$$
$$90 = 2 \times 3 \times 5 \times 3$$
$$210 = 2 \times 3 \times 5 \times 7$$

The least common multiple of 60, 90, and 210 must contain the prime factors 2, 2, 3, and 5 in order to contain 60; it must contain the additional prime factor 3, in order to contain 90, and the additional prime factor 7, in order to contain 210.

Therefore, $2 \times 2 \times 3 \times 5 \times 3 \times 7$, or $1260 = $ l. c. m. of 60, 90, and 210.

The least common multiple of two or more numbers is the product of all their different prime factors each taken the greatest number of times it occurs in any one of them.

Exercise 6

Find the least common multiple of:

1. 28 and 42. 2. 84 and 96. 3. 63 and 84.

4. 66 and 99. 5. 56 and 120. 6. 75 and 125.

7. 52 and 130. 8. 105 and 135. 9. 154 and 242.

10. 45, 75, and 90. 11. 52, 78, and 104.

12. 30, 90, and 150. 13. 56, 70, and 84.

14. 110, 275, and 605 15. 65, 91, and 143.

16. 91, 117, and 130. 17. 108, 180, and 243.

PART II

Exercise 2, page 160

1. 91,596.   2. 97,817.   3. 14,392.
4. 152,772.   5. 2,930,893,000.   6. 5,898,089,000 ; 353,337,000.
7. 10,440,000.   8. 70,912,000.   9. 5,016,000 ; 1,254,000.
10. 12,872 lb.   11. $2092.   12. $540.

Exercise 3, page 162

1. 42,480.   2. 77,050.   3. 92,115.   4. 37.
5. 1733.   6. $480.   7. 3125.   8. 8 ; 6900.
9. $2.   10. silage, 2100 ; hay, 1120 ; corn, 420 ; meal, 70.
11. $1110.

Exercise 5, page 168

1. 2, 2, 3, 13.   2. 2, 7, 13.   3. 2, 2, 2, 5, 7.
4. 2, 3, 3, 5, 7.   5. 3, 5, 7, 7.   6. 3, 3, 5, 17.
7. 7, 11, 13.   8. 2, 3, 3, 5, 5, 7.   9. 2.
10. 2, 5, 10.   11. 3, 5, 15.   12. 2, 11, 22.
13. 2, 3, 5, 6, 10, 15, 30.   14. 2, 5, 7, 10, 14, 35, 70.   15. 8.
16. 14.   17. 7.   18. 18.
19. 25.   20. 56.   21. 7.
22. 8.   23. 10.   24. 26.
25. 35.   26. 48.   27. 108.
28. 192.

Exercise 6, page 169

1. 84.   2. 672.   3. 252.   4. 198.   5. 840.   6. 375.
7. 260.   8. 945.   9. 1694.   10. 450.   11. 312.   12. 450.
13. 840.   14. 6050.   15. 5005.   16. 8190.   17. 4860.

Exercise 7, page 170

1. 519 mi.   2. 10,267,417 bales.   3. 15 ¢.   4. 6.
5. $1.64.   6. 5.   7. 720 ; 2.   8. 3200 ft.
9. $60.   10. 97.   11. $2960.   12. 2, 3, 5.
14. $54.75.   15. 1,600,000.   16. 1000.   17. 10,000.
18. 24.   19. 30.   20. 4 ¢.

Supplements

"The principal defect of
Egyptian arithmetic was the
lack of a simple comprehensive
symbolism, a defect which not
even the Greeks were able to
remove."
~ p. 15 (The Egyptians)

Explorations – Basic Addition Facts

Explorations – Basic Multiplication Facts

Build Back Better November 2021 Proposal

Exploration - Basic Addition Facts - MAKELIST

Wednesday, December 8, 2021   11:24 PM

Lists are displayed as {}s. Lists allow us to do multiple calculation with one command line.
Addition Basic Facts Table - Calculator Partial Table (two methods- Adding Two List - Adding Inside a List)

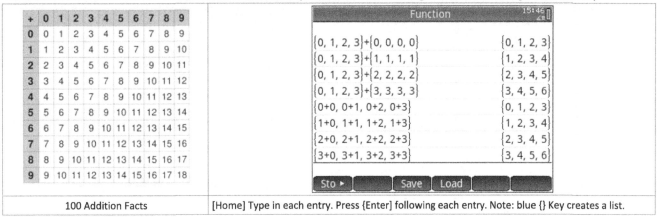

| | 100 Addition Facts | [Home] Type in each entry. Press {Enter} following each entry. Note: blue {} Key creates a list. |

To display MAKELIST command's Help - press [Toolbox] - if necessary select soft key [Catlg] letter - press M (+/- key). With curser in the MAKELIST command - press [Help]. Home View MAKELIST uses upper only. Press [ALPHA] [x] (multiplication key) to return upper case "X". In CAS View same keys will return lower case "x".

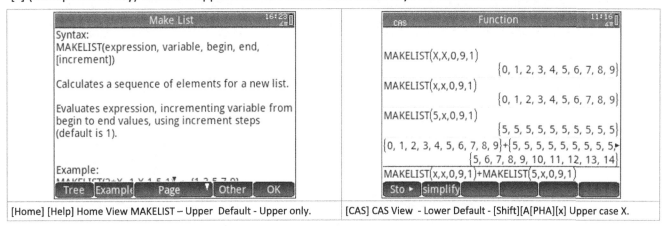

| [Home] [Help] Home View MAKELIST – Upper Default - Upper only. | [CAS] CAS View - Lower Default - [Shift][A[PHA][x] Upper case X. |

Exploration - Basic Multiplication Facts - MAKELIST

Monday, December 13, 2021   10:09 AM

Lists, shown as {}s, allow us to do multiple calculation with one command line. Multiplication Basic Facts Table - Calculator Partial Table (two methods- Multiplying Two List - Multiplying Inside a List)

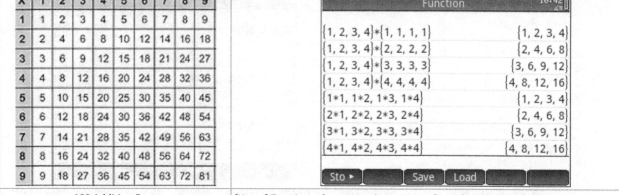

	100 Addition Facts	[Home] Type in each entry as shown. Press {Enter}. Note: blue {} Key creates a list.

To display MAKELIST command's Help - press [Toolbox] - if necessary select soft key [Catlg] letter - press M (+/- key). With curser in the MAKELIST command - press [Help]. Home View MAKELIST uses upper only. Press [ALPHA] [x] (multiplication key) to return upper case "X". In CAS View same keys will return lower case "x".

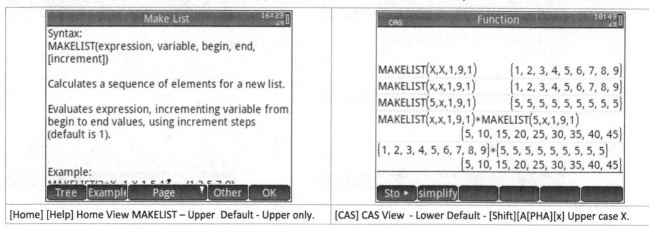

[Home] [Help] Home View MAKELIST – Upper Default - Upper only.	[CAS] CAS View - Lower Default - [Shift][A[PHA][x] Upper case X.

Build Back Better November 2021 Proposal

Saturday, December 11, 2021   12:17 PM

Breakdown of $1.75 trillion Build Back Better framework (in $billion) In World Economy News 20/11/2021

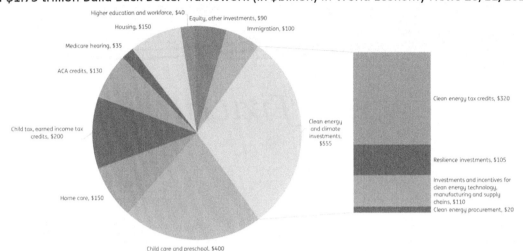

Cost of clean energy and climate investments $550 billion. What is the cost of all other items? ($1.195 trillion)
Calculator command line entry : NumberE9 - billion, NumberE12 - trillion (Use [EEX] for E). Verify $555 billion.

Prime Command line entry	Prime History screen	Function 13:47
Method 1 (top two entries)	Method 1 – Entry's Result	
320E9+105E9+110E9+20E9	555,000,000,000	
1.75E12-[Copy] history	1.195E12	320,000,000,000+105,000,000,000+110,000,000,0 **** 555,000,000,000
555,000,000,000		1.75E12−555,000,000,000 1.195E12
		320+105+110+20 555
Method 2 (bottom two entries)	Method 2 – Bottom 2 Results	1,750−555 1,195
320+105+110+20	555	
1750-555 (see below)+	1,195 (see below)++	Sto ▸ Save Load
+ Method 2 - For input translate 1.75 trillion to 1750 billion	++ Method 2 - Read 1,195 billion as 1.195 trillion	All numberE9s are displayed in ordinary notation. All numberE12s are displayed as their self.

2

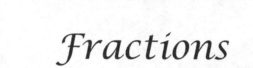

Fractions

> "It seems to me, that if statesmen had a little more arithmetic, or were accustomed to calculation, wars would be much less frequent. "
> ~ Benjamin Franklin

Introductory Exercises and Definitions

Addition and Subtraction

Multiplication and Division

Introductory Exercises and Definitions

Wednesday, December 8, 2021   11:35 PM

Halves, Fourths, and Eighths. For the solve command - press [Toolbox] - if necessary select soft key [CAS] - [3Solve] [1Solve]. (solve is CAS only).

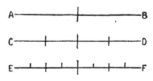 Line AB, CD, EF divided into how many equal parts? {2, 4, 8} How many eighths are there in 1/4 ? in 1/2 ? In 3/4 ? {2, 4, 6}	**Multiply left side of equality by 1 equivalents - 2/2, 4/4, 8/8** **Supply the missing numbers** $1 = \dfrac{}{2}$ $1 = \dfrac{}{4}$ $\dfrac{1}{2} = \dfrac{}{4}$ $1 = \dfrac{}{8}$ $\dfrac{1}{2} = \dfrac{}{8}$ $\dfrac{1}{4} = \dfrac{}{8}$ $\dfrac{2}{4} = \dfrac{}{8}$ $\dfrac{3}{4} = \dfrac{}{8}$ {2, 4, 2, 8, 4, 2, 4, 6} Prime use CAS View solve command: $\text{solve}\left(1 = \dfrac{x}{2}\right)$ {2}

Definitions

The number of parts a fraction is divided into form the **denominator**. The number of units taken to make a fraction is called the **numerator**.
 	
 A fraction whose numerator is less than its denominator is called a **proper fraction**.
    Thus, 1/2 and 3/4 are proper fractions.
 	
 A fraction whose numerator is equal to, or greater than, its denominator is called an **improper fraction**.
    Thus, 4/4 and 5/4 are improper fractions.
 	
 A number made up of a whole number and a fraction combined is called a **mixed numeral**.
    Thus, 2 1/2 means 2+1/2 is a mixed numeral.
	Divide left side of equality by 1 equivalents - 2/2, 4/4, 8/8
	 It is generally known that multiplying both numerator and denominator by the same number, that is an 1 equivalent, does not change the fraction. Not known as well that dividing both numerator and denominator by the same number, that is an 1 equivalent, does not change the fraction.
	
	 Supply the missing numbers
	
	 $\dfrac{8}{16} = \dfrac{}{2}$ $\dfrac{2}{8} = \dfrac{}{4}$ $\dfrac{4}{16} = \dfrac{}{4}$ $\dfrac{4}{16} = \dfrac{}{8}$
	
	 $\dfrac{2}{4} = \dfrac{}{2}$ $\dfrac{8}{8} = \dfrac{}{2}$ $\dfrac{2}{16} = \dfrac{}{8}$ $\dfrac{6}{8} = \dfrac{}{4}$
	
	 {1, 1, 1, 2, 1, 2, 1, 3 }
	
	 Prime use CAS View solve command: $\text{solve}\left(\dfrac{6}{8} = \dfrac{x}{4}\right)$ {3}

44   **FRACTIONS**

FRACTIONS

INTRODUCTORY EXERCISES AND DEFINITIONS

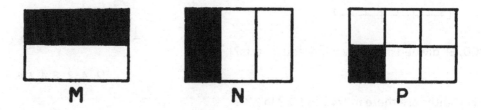

1. What part of M is black? what part of N? what part of P? What part of M is white? what part of N? what part of P?

2. How many halves are there in one? how many thirds? how many sixths?

3. How many sixths are there in one half? in one third? in two halves? in two thirds? in three thirds?

4. How many sixths of a rectangle are there in N and one sixth of P together?

41. Any one thing is called a **unit**.

42. Any one of the equal parts of a unit is called a **fractional unit**.

Thus, one half and one third are fractional units.

43. Any number of equal fractional units is a **fraction**.

Thus, one half, two halves, two thirds, and seven sixths are fractions.

44. The number of equal parts into which a unit is divided to form fractional units is the **denominator**, and

Addition and Subtraction

Wednesday, December 8, 2021   11:35 PM

For Prime addition and subtraction move curser out of the first fraction before pressing operation.

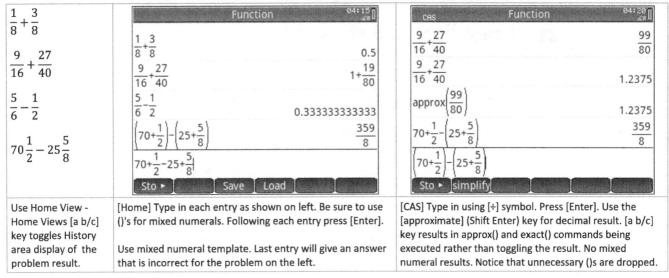

$\dfrac{1}{8}+\dfrac{3}{8}$		
$\dfrac{9}{16}+\dfrac{27}{40}$		
$\dfrac{5}{6}-\dfrac{1}{2}$		
$70\dfrac{1}{2}-25\dfrac{5}{8}$		

| Use Home View - Home Views [a b/c] key toggles History area display of the problem result. | [Home] Type in each entry as shown on left. Be sure to use ()'s for mixed numerals. Following each entry press [Enter].\n\nUse mixed numeral template. Last entry will give an answer that is incorrect for the problem on the left. | [CAS] Type in using [÷] symbol. Press [Enter]. Use the [approximate] (Shift Enter) key for decimal result. [a b/c] key results in approx() and exact() commands being executed rather than toggling the result. No mixed numeral results. Notice that unnecessary ()s are dropped. |

If a man owes me \$37 1/2 and gives me three ten-dollar bills and \$1 3/4 worth of quarters, how much does he still owe me?

Method 1 makes use of nested grouping. Prime uses parenthesis only.
Method 2 subtracts twice. (copied mixed numeral changed to decimal)
Method 3 does part of calculation in our head.

Toggled all results to mixed numeral form.

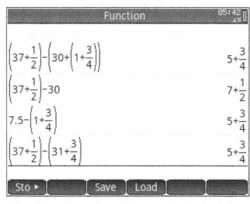

[Home} Type in as shown. Three methods of solution.

58   **FRACTIONS**

Addition of Fractions that are not Similar

62. Draw lines and show that:

1. $\frac{1}{2} + \frac{1}{4} = \frac{2}{4} + \frac{1}{4} = \frac{3}{4}$.

What is the l. c. d. of $\frac{1}{2}$ and $\frac{1}{4}$?

2. $\frac{1}{3} + \frac{1}{2} = \frac{2}{6} + \frac{3}{6} = \frac{5}{6}$.

What is the l. c. d. of $\frac{1}{3}$ and $\frac{1}{2}$?

3. $\frac{2}{3} + \frac{3}{4} = \frac{8}{12} + \frac{9}{12} = \frac{17}{12}$, or $1\frac{5}{12}$.

What is the l. c. d. of $\frac{2}{3}$ and $\frac{3}{4}$?

To add fractions with unlike denominators, reduce them to similar fractions having the least common denominator, and add the similar fractions.

Exercise 44

Find the sum:

1. $\frac{1}{2} + \frac{1}{4}$ 2. $\frac{1}{2} + \frac{1}{8}$ 3. $\frac{1}{4} + \frac{1}{8}$

4. $\frac{1}{3} + \frac{1}{6}$ 5. $\frac{1}{3} + \frac{1}{9}$ 6. $\frac{1}{4} + \frac{1}{12}$

7. $\frac{1}{6} + \frac{1}{12}$ 8. $\frac{1}{5} + \frac{1}{10}$ 9. $\frac{1}{5} + \frac{1}{15}$

10. $\frac{1}{2} + \frac{1}{3}$ 11. $\frac{1}{6} + \frac{1}{4}$ 12. $\frac{1}{2} + \frac{1}{5}$

13. $\frac{1}{3} + \frac{1}{5}$ 14. $\frac{1}{4} + \frac{1}{5}$ 15. $\frac{1}{6} + \frac{1}{8}$

16. $\frac{1}{6} + \frac{1}{9}$ 17. $\frac{1}{8} + \frac{1}{12}$ 18. $\frac{1}{4} + \frac{1}{10}$

19. $\frac{1}{2} + \frac{2}{3}$ 20. $\frac{1}{2} + \frac{3}{4}$ 21. $\frac{1}{2} + \frac{3}{8}$

22. $\frac{2}{3} + \frac{1}{6}$ 23. $\frac{2}{3} + \frac{5}{6}$ 24. $\frac{3}{4} + \frac{5}{8}$

25. $\frac{3}{4} + \frac{7}{8}$ 26. $\frac{2}{3} + \frac{3}{8}$ 27. $\frac{3}{4} + \frac{5}{6}$

62   FRACTIONS

Exercise 47

Find the difference of :

1. $\frac{3}{4}$ and $\frac{2}{3}$ 2. $\frac{4}{5}$ and $\frac{3}{4}$ 3. $\frac{7}{8}$ and $\frac{5}{6}$

4. $\frac{7}{12}$ and $\frac{3}{8}$ 5. $\frac{5}{4}$ and $\frac{5}{6}$ 6. $\frac{3}{2}$ and $\frac{2}{5}$

7. $\frac{15}{16}$ and $\frac{3}{4}$ 8. $\frac{17}{30}$ and $\frac{13}{45}$ 9. $\frac{7}{24}$ and $\frac{5}{36}$

10. $\frac{8}{25}$ and $\frac{3}{50}$ 11. $\frac{8}{9}$ and $\frac{2}{3}$ 12. $\frac{5}{6}$ and $\frac{7}{9}$

13. $\frac{11}{27}$ and $\frac{5}{18}$ 14. $\frac{13}{50}$ and $\frac{4}{75}$ 15. $\frac{13}{24}$ and $\frac{13}{40}$

Problems

Exercise 48

1. If A can do $\frac{1}{2}$ of a piece of work in one day, B $\frac{1}{4}$ of it in one day, and C $\frac{1}{8}$ of it in one day, what part of it can they together do in one day?

$\frac{1}{2}$ = the part A can do in a day.
$\frac{1}{4}$ = the part B can do in a day.
$\frac{1}{8}$ = the part C can do in a day.
$\therefore \frac{1}{2} + \frac{1}{4} + \frac{1}{8}$, or $\frac{7}{8}$ = the part they together can do in a day.

NOTE. — The symbol $\therefore$ is read **therefore.**

2. A can do $\frac{2}{3}$ of a piece of work in one day, and A and B together can do $\frac{7}{8}$ of it; what part can B do in one day?

$\frac{2}{3}$ = the part A can do in one day.
$\frac{7}{8}$ = the part A and B together can do in one day.
$\therefore \frac{7}{8} - \frac{2}{3}$, or $\frac{5}{24}$ = the part B can do in one day.

3. If a man does $\frac{1}{6}$ of a piece of work one day and $\frac{1}{4}$ of it another day, what part of it has he then done?

iv

ANSWERS

Exercise 42, page 56

2. $\frac{8}{12}$, $\frac{9}{12}$.   3. $\frac{15}{20}$, $\frac{16}{20}$.   4. $\frac{24}{30}$, $\frac{25}{30}$.

5. $\frac{13}{15}$, $\frac{9}{15}$.   6. $\frac{6}{10}$, $\frac{7}{10}$.   7. $\frac{11}{18}$, $\frac{12}{18}$.

8. $\frac{6}{12}$, $\frac{4}{12}$, $\frac{1}{12}$.   9. $\frac{4}{12}$, $\frac{3}{12}$, $\frac{2}{12}$.   10. $\frac{12}{18}$, $\frac{1}{18}$, $\frac{4}{18}$.

11. $\frac{12}{20}$, $\frac{10}{20}$, $\frac{15}{20}$.   12. $\frac{21}{24}$, $\frac{10}{24}$, $\frac{14}{24}$.   13. $\frac{15}{18}$, $\frac{9}{18}$, $\frac{4}{18}$.

14. $\frac{4}{10}$, $\frac{7}{10}$, $\frac{5}{10}$.   15. $\frac{13}{30}$, $\frac{9}{30}$, $\frac{5}{30}$.   16. $\frac{14}{16}$, $\frac{5}{16}$, $\frac{12}{16}$.

17. $\frac{5}{30}$, $\frac{18}{30}$, $\frac{12}{30}$.   18. $\frac{11}{24}$, $\frac{9}{24}$, $\frac{20}{24}$.   19. $\frac{20}{50}$, $\frac{2}{50}$, $\frac{8}{50}$.

20. $\frac{5}{35}$, $\frac{27}{35}$, $\frac{18}{35}$.   21. $\frac{9}{12}$, $\frac{10}{12}$, $\frac{12}{12}$.   22. $\frac{14}{80}$, $\frac{50}{80}$, $\frac{32}{80}$.

23. $\frac{24}{56}$, $\frac{42}{56}$, $\frac{14}{56}$.   24. $\frac{20}{48}$, $\frac{42}{48}$, $\frac{9}{48}$.   25. $\frac{12}{100}$, $\frac{6}{100}$, $\frac{15}{100}$.

26. $\frac{30}{120}$, $\frac{24}{120}$, $\frac{20}{120}$, $\frac{15}{120}$.   27. $\frac{6}{12}$, $\frac{8}{12}$, $\frac{9}{12}$, $\frac{10}{12}$.   28. $\frac{12}{20}$, $\frac{8}{20}$, $\frac{15}{20}$, $\frac{14}{20}$.

Exercise 44, page 58

1. $\frac{3}{4}$.   2. $\frac{2}{5}$.   3. $\frac{3}{8}$.   4. $\frac{1}{2}$.   5. $\frac{4}{5}$.   6. $\frac{1}{6}$.   7. $\frac{1}{4}$.

8. $\frac{1}{10}$.   9. $\frac{4}{15}$.   10. $\frac{5}{6}$.   11. $\frac{5}{12}$.   12. $\frac{7}{10}$.   13. $\frac{8}{15}$.   14. $\frac{9}{20}$.

15. $\frac{7}{24}$.   16. $\frac{5}{12}$.   17. $\frac{5}{24}$.   18. $\frac{7}{20}$.   19. $1\frac{1}{6}$.   20. $1\frac{1}{4}$.   21. $\frac{7}{8}$.

22. $\frac{3}{5}$.   23. $1\frac{1}{2}$.   24. $1\frac{3}{8}$.   25. $1\frac{3}{5}$.   26. $1\frac{1}{24}$.   27. $1\frac{7}{12}$.

Exercise 45, page 60

1. $1\frac{7}{24}$.   2. $1\frac{1}{10}$.   3. $1\frac{11}{24}$.   4. $1\frac{17}{18}$.   5. $2\frac{4}{45}$.   6. $2\frac{4}{45}$.   7. $1\frac{1}{32}$.

8. $1\frac{3}{24}$.   9. $\frac{23}{24}$.   10. $1\frac{17}{72}$.   11. $1\frac{18}{35}$.   12. $1\frac{14}{45}$.   13. $1\frac{11}{100}$.   14. $1\frac{8}{50}$.

15. $\frac{23}{56}$.   16. $\frac{53}{80}$.   17. $1\frac{13}{18}$.   18. $2\frac{1}{8}$.   19. $2\frac{1}{6}$.   20. $2\frac{7}{45}$.   21. $1\frac{17}{48}$.

22. $\frac{47}{48}$.   23. $1\frac{11}{14}$.   24. $1\frac{14}{15}$.

Exercise 47, page 62

1. $\frac{1}{12}$.   2. $\frac{1}{20}$.   3. $\frac{1}{24}$.   4. $\frac{5}{24}$.   5. $\frac{5}{12}$.   6. $1\frac{1}{10}$.   7. $\frac{3}{16}$.

8. $\frac{5}{18}$.   9. $\frac{11}{72}$.   10. $\frac{13}{50}$.   11. $\frac{2}{3}$.   12. $\frac{1}{18}$.   13. $\frac{7}{54}$.   14. $\frac{81}{150}$.

15. $\frac{13}{60}$.

Exercise 48, page 62

3. $\frac{9}{20}$.   4. $\frac{1}{2}$.   5. $1\frac{1}{8}$ bu.   6. $1\frac{1}{12}$ A.   7. $1\frac{5}{8}$ A.   8. $\frac{13}{18}$ yd.

9. $\frac{1}{8}$.   10. $2\frac{7}{24}$ mi.   11. $\$1\frac{1}{4}$.   12. $\frac{7}{10}$.   13. $1\frac{3}{8}$ gal.   14. $1\frac{1}{8}$ A.

15. $\$1\frac{17}{20}$.   16. $\$\frac{4}{5}$.   17. $\$\frac{3}{4}$.

Exercise 49, page 64

1. $5\frac{11}{16}$.   2. $13\frac{11}{12}$.   3. $19\frac{1}{24}$.   4. $17\frac{25}{32}$.   5. $44\frac{1}{6}$.   6. $89\frac{7}{48}$.

7. $41\frac{1}{3}$.   8. $47\frac{11}{12}$.   9. $117\frac{31}{42}$.   10. $54\frac{7}{12}$.   11. $104\frac{11}{24}$.   12. $116\frac{1}{4}$.

13. $66\frac{2}{3}$.   14. $54\frac{1}{6}$.   15. $67\frac{1}{4}$.   16. $16\frac{2}{3}$.   17. $44\frac{4}{7}$.   18. $52\frac{11}{18}$.

19. $19\frac{5}{8}$.   20. $23\frac{17}{17}$.   21. $11\frac{1}{4}$.   22. $88\frac{1}{2}$.   23. $19\frac{5}{42}$.   24. $62\frac{3}{4}$.

Find the difference:

13. $100 - 33\frac{1}{3}$ 14. $66\frac{2}{3} - 12\frac{1}{2}$

15. $86\frac{1}{2} - 18\frac{3}{4}$ 16. $33\frac{1}{3} - 16\frac{2}{3}$

17. $70\frac{1}{2} - 25\frac{5}{8}$ 18. $85\frac{1}{8} - 32\frac{7}{16}$

19. $32\frac{5}{9} - 12\frac{2}{3}$ 20. $56\frac{5}{6} - 32\frac{8}{9}$

21. $25\frac{7}{12} - 13\frac{5}{6}$ 22. $128\frac{3}{10} - 39\frac{4}{5}$

23. $47\frac{3}{14} - 28\frac{2}{21}$ 24. $100\frac{1}{9} - 37\frac{3}{8}$

Problems

Exercise 50

1. A man owned $37\frac{1}{2}$ acres of land and bought $32\frac{3}{4}$ acres more; how much had he then?

2. The four sides of a field measure $42\frac{1}{2}$ rods, 31 rods, $26\frac{1}{2}$ rods, and $38\frac{1}{2}$ rods; what is the distance around the field?

3. Find the weight of four hams, whose weights are $12\frac{3}{4}$ lb., $14\frac{1}{2}$ lb., $16\frac{3}{4}$ lb., and $15\frac{1}{2}$ lb.

4. What is the distance around a room whose length is $18\frac{3}{4}$ ft. and width $15\frac{3}{4}$ ft.?

5. A woman bought $37\frac{1}{2}$ yd. muslin and has used $18\frac{3}{4}$ yd. of it; how much remains?

6. From 40 yd. of carpet, 3 pieces were sold, whose lengths were $10\frac{1}{2}$ yd., $7\frac{3}{4}$ yd., and $8\frac{3}{4}$ yd.; how much remains?

7. How much change should a woman receive from 2 fifty-dollar bills given in payment of a bill of $\$72\frac{1}{2}$?

Exercise 50, page 65

1. $70\frac{1}{4}$ A. 2. $138\frac{1}{2}$ rd. 3. $59\frac{1}{2}$ lb. 4. 69 ft. 5. $18\frac{3}{4}$ yd.
6. 13 yd. 7. \$$27\frac{1}{2}$. 8. $24\frac{1}{4}$ lb. 9. $27\frac{1}{2}$ gal. 10. $188\frac{1}{2}$ yd.
11. $7\frac{1}{3}$ A. 12. \$20. 13. $62\frac{1}{2}$. 14. $87\frac{1}{2}$. 15. $\frac{23}{30}$.

Exercise 51, page 66

1. $37\frac{9}{50}$ T. 2. $13\frac{13}{24}$ ft. 3. $53\frac{1}{4}$ mi. 4. $\frac{5}{72}$. 5. $\frac{3}{16}$.
6. 8 lb. 7. $63\frac{1}{2}$ lb. 8. \$12.50. 9. 200. 10. $\frac{9}{10}$, $\frac{8}{9}$, $\frac{5}{6}$, $\frac{9}{15}$, $\frac{1}{2}$.
11. \$$4\frac{1}{4}$. 12. $58\frac{1}{3}$. 13. $60\frac{3}{4}$ ft. 14. $54\frac{1}{4}$. 15. \$$3\frac{3}{4}$.
16. $5\frac{1}{2}$ in. 17. 113 ft. 18. 25. 19. $88\frac{2}{3}$. 20. \$$187\frac{1}{2}$.
21. \$$3\frac{3}{20}$. 22. $45\frac{11}{12}$. 23. $2\frac{2}{3}$ A. 24. \$$1\frac{1}{2}$. 25. \$126.
26. $\frac{1}{4}$. 27. $\frac{9}{10}$. 28. \$$22\frac{1}{4}$. 29. \$$87\frac{1}{2}$. 30. 139.

Exercise 53, page 70

1. $1\frac{1}{2}$ in. 2. \$$\frac{1}{2}$. 3. 10¢. 4. \$1. 5. 1 qt.
6. $\frac{1}{2}$ lb. 7. $1\frac{1}{2}$ in. 8. $\frac{3}{4}$. 9. 7 A. 10. $2\frac{5}{8}$ qt.

Exercise 55, page 72

1. $4\frac{1}{2}$ yd. 2. $36\frac{3}{4}$ mi. 3. $2\frac{1}{4}$ bu. 4. $9\frac{1}{6}$ min. 5. $7\frac{1}{2}$ ft.
6. $37\frac{1}{2}$ yd. 7. \$5. 8. 39¢. 9. 50¢. 10. \$18.
11. 33¢. 12. 20¢. 13. 40¢. 14. 26¢. 15. \$$4\frac{1}{2}$.
16. \$$12\frac{1}{2}$.

Exercise 57, page 75

1. $2\frac{2}{3}$. 2. $\frac{4}{5}$. 3. $\frac{5}{16}$. 4. $\frac{1}{2}$. 5. $\frac{4}{15}$. 6. $\frac{49}{72}$.
7. $1\frac{1}{9}$. 8. $\frac{15}{28}$. 9. $\frac{2}{5}$. 10. $1\frac{3}{5}$. 11. $3\frac{6}{7}$. 12. $\frac{2}{3}$.
13. $1\frac{1}{20}$. 14. $2\frac{26}{243}$. 15. $\frac{8}{35}$. 16. $1\frac{1}{9}$. 17. $\frac{1}{6}$. 18. $\frac{35}{108}$.
19. $1\frac{1}{3}$. 20. 1. 21. $1\frac{4}{5}$. 22. $\frac{72}{145}$. 23. $\frac{4}{7}$. 24. $\frac{4}{5}$.
25. $\frac{1}{6}$. 26. $\frac{3}{8}$. 27. $1\frac{1}{2}$. 28. $\frac{2}{3}$. 29. $\frac{1}{2}$. 30. $2\frac{1}{2}$.
31. $\frac{6}{55}$. 32. 1. 33. $1\frac{1}{3}$.

Exercise 58, page 76

1. 1. 2. $1\frac{3}{5}$. 3. $3\frac{6}{7}$. 4. $\frac{2}{3}$.
5. $\frac{11}{18}$. 6. $2\frac{17}{32}$. 7. $1\frac{17}{27}$. 8. $3\frac{3}{4}$.
9. 2. 10. $16\frac{1}{2}$. 11. $18\frac{1}{8}$. 12. $11\frac{3}{8}$.
13. $24\frac{3}{7}$. 14. 65. 15. $10\frac{11}{16}$. 16. 2079.
17. $3029\frac{1}{3}$. 18. $4912\frac{1}{2}$. 19. $5240\frac{1}{4}$. 20. $8319\frac{1}{6}$.
21. $11318\frac{2}{5}$. 22. 14742. 23. 2958. 24. $7598\frac{1}{3}$.

Multiplication and Division

Tuesday, December 28, 2021   12:37 AM

For Prime multiplication and division move curser out of the first fraction before pressing operation.

MULTIPLY AND DIVIDE		
$4\ by\ \dfrac{3}{8}$ $\dfrac{9}{16}\ by\ \dfrac{27}{40}$ $\dfrac{5}{6}\ by\ 2$ $70\dfrac{1}{2}\ by\ 25\dfrac{5}{8}$	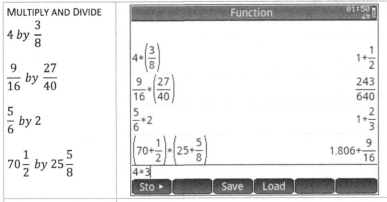	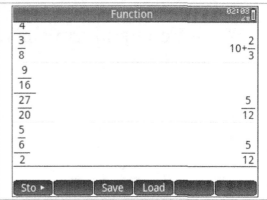
Use Home View - Home Views [a b/c] key toggles History area display of the problem result.	[Home] Type in each entry as multiplication. Use ()'s when necessary. Example: Command line shown needs ()'s. Multiplicand plus proper and improper fractions inside ()'s can use the [÷] key to enter the fraction.	[Home] Type in each entry as division. Use ()'s when necessary. First entry 4÷(3÷8). Second entry (9÷16) ÷(27÷20). Third entry (5÷6)÷2. Last problem (70 1/2)÷(25 5/6) is shown below. The result is 2 154/205. For mixed numerals use fraction template.

If a laborer was paid $200 for 1 1/4 days' work, what should he be paid for 2 1/2 days' work? ($400)

Two Steps

Dollars per day   - $200 \div 1\dfrac{1}{4} = 160$

2 1/2 days' pay   - $160 \times 2\dfrac{1}{2} = 400$

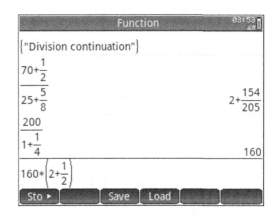

Later we will work problem by Ratio and Proportion's direct variation.
1 1/4 day : 2 1/2 days = 200 dollars : x dollars

$$\dfrac{1\frac{1}{4}}{2\frac{1}{2}} = \dfrac{200}{x}\quad means\ product = exteme\ product\ \ 500 = 1\frac{1}{4}\ x\ \ x = \$400$$

[Home} Type in entries. Be sure to use ()'s and fraction template as needed. Command line result is 400.

Exercise 57

Copy and multiply, expressing the answers in the simplest form:

1. $\frac{4}{5} \times \frac{10}{3}$ 2. $\frac{4}{3} \times \frac{3}{8}$ 3. $\frac{5}{6} \times \frac{3}{8}$

4. $\frac{2}{3} \times \frac{3}{4}$ 5. $\frac{2}{9} \times \frac{6}{5}$ 6. $\frac{14}{15} \times \frac{35}{48}$

7. $\frac{25}{24} \times \frac{16}{15}$ 8. $\frac{9}{16} \times \frac{20}{21}$ 9. $\frac{2}{3} \times \frac{3}{5}$

10. $\frac{3}{5} \times \frac{8}{3}$ 11. $\frac{6}{7} \times \frac{9}{2}$ 12. $\frac{3}{8} \times \frac{16}{9}$

13. $\frac{39}{40} \times \frac{28}{26}$ 14. $\frac{32}{9} \times \frac{16}{27}$ 15. $\frac{12}{25} \times \frac{10}{21}$

16. $\frac{7}{12} \times \frac{40}{21}$ 17. $\frac{9}{16} \times \frac{8}{27}$ 18. $\frac{7}{15} \times \frac{25}{36}$

19. $\frac{44}{45} \times \frac{30}{22}$ 20. $\frac{11}{15} \times \frac{45}{33}$ 21. $\frac{15}{16} \times \frac{48}{25}$

22. $\frac{18}{25} \times \frac{20}{29}$ 23. $\frac{14}{15} \times \frac{30}{49}$ 24. $\frac{15}{16} \times \frac{64}{75}$

25. $\frac{32}{33} \times \frac{11}{64}$ 26. $\frac{11}{14} \times \frac{21}{44}$ 27. $\frac{45}{32} \times \frac{16}{15}$

28. $\frac{32}{45} \times \frac{15}{16}$ 29. $\frac{100}{3} \times \frac{3}{200}$ 30. $\frac{125}{2} \times \frac{3}{75}$

31. $\frac{9}{25} \times \frac{10}{33}$ 32. $\frac{7}{75} \times \frac{150}{14}$ 33. $\frac{1}{50} \times \frac{200}{3}$

Multiplying by a Mixed Number

73. 1. When the multiplier, or the multiplier and the multiplicand both are small mixed numbers, the product may be readily found; thus,

Multiply $2\frac{2}{5}$ by $3\frac{1}{4}$.

$$2\frac{2}{5} \times 3\frac{1}{4} = \frac{\overset{3}{\cancel{12}}}{5} \times \frac{13}{\cancel{4}} = \frac{39}{5} = 7\frac{4}{5}$$

ANSWERS

Exercise 50, page 65

1. $70\frac{1}{4}$ A. 2. $138\frac{1}{2}$ rd. 3. $59\frac{1}{2}$ lb. 4. 69 ft. 5. $18\frac{1}{4}$ yd.
6. 18 yd. 7. $27\frac{1}{2}$. 8. $24\frac{1}{2}$ lb. 9. $27\frac{1}{2}$ gal. 10. $188\frac{1}{2}$ yd.
11. $7\frac{1}{8}$ A. 12. $20. 13. $62\frac{1}{2}$. 14. $87\frac{1}{2}$. 15. $\frac{24}{30}$.

Exercise 51, page 66

1. $3\frac{7}{16}$ T. 2. $13\frac{11}{24}$ ft. 3. $53\frac{1}{4}$ mi. 4. $\frac{5}{72}$. 5. $\frac{3}{16}$.
6. 8 lb. 7. $63\frac{1}{2}$ lb. 8. $12.50. 9. 200. 10. $\frac{9}{10}, \frac{3}{5}, \frac{5}{6}, \frac{9}{15}, \frac{1}{2}$.
11. $4\frac{1}{4}$. 12. $58\frac{1}{8}$. 13. $60\frac{3}{4}$ ft. 14. $54\frac{1}{4}$. 15. $3\frac{3}{4}$.
16. $5\frac{1}{2}$ in. 17. 113 ft. 18. 25. 19. $88\frac{3}{4}$. 20. $187\frac{1}{2}$.
21. $3\frac{9}{20}$. 22. $45\frac{11}{12}$. 23. $2\frac{1}{4}$ A. 24. $1\frac{1}{4}$. 25. $126.
26. $\frac{1}{4}$. 27. $\frac{9}{10}$. 28. $22\frac{1}{4}$. 29. $87\frac{1}{2}$. 30. 139.

Exercise 53, page 70

1. $1\frac{1}{2}$ in. 2. $\frac{1}{2}$. 3. 10 ¢. 4. $1. 5. 1 qt.
6. $\frac{1}{2}$ lb. 7. $1\frac{1}{2}$ in. 8. $\frac{3}{4}$. 9. 7 A. 10. $2\frac{5}{8}$ qt.

Exercise 55, page 72

1. $4\frac{1}{2}$ yd. 2. $36\frac{3}{4}$ mi. 3. $2\frac{1}{4}$ bu. 4. $9\frac{1}{8}$ min. 5. $7\frac{1}{2}$ ft.
6. $37\frac{1}{2}$ yd. 7. $5. 8. 39 ¢. 9. 50 ¢. 10. $18.
11. 33 ¢. 12. 20 ¢. 13. 40 ¢. 14. 26 ¢. 15. $4\frac{1}{2}$.
16. $12\frac{1}{2}$.

Exercise 57, page 75

1. $2\frac{4}{5}$. 2. $\frac{4}{5}$. 3. $\frac{5}{16}$. 4. $\frac{1}{2}$. 5. $\frac{4}{15}$. 6. $4\frac{2}{3}$.
7. $1\frac{1}{5}$. 8. $\frac{15}{28}$. 9. $\frac{3}{4}$. 10. $1\frac{3}{5}$. 11. $3\frac{4}{7}$. 12. $\frac{2}{5}$.
13. $1\frac{1}{20}$. 14. $2\frac{26}{245}$. 15. $\frac{8}{35}$. 16. $1\frac{1}{4}$. 17. $\frac{1}{6}$. 18. $\frac{35}{108}$.
19. $1\frac{1}{5}$. 20. 1. 21. $1\frac{4}{5}$. 22. $\frac{72}{145}$. 23. $\frac{4}{7}$. 24. $\frac{4}{5}$.
25. $\frac{1}{6}$. 26. $\frac{3}{8}$. 27. $1\frac{1}{2}$. 28. $\frac{3}{4}$. 29. $\frac{1}{2}$. 30. $2\frac{1}{2}$.
31. $\frac{6}{55}$. 32. 1. 33. $1\frac{1}{3}$.

Exercise 58, page 76

1. 1. 2. $1\frac{4}{5}$. 3. $3\frac{4}{7}$. 4. $\frac{3}{4}$.
5. $\frac{11}{13}$. 6. $2\frac{14}{31}$. 7. $1\frac{14}{17}$. 8. $3\frac{1}{4}$.
9. 2. 10. $16\frac{1}{4}$. 11. $18\frac{1}{4}$. 12. $11\frac{4}{5}$.
13. $24\frac{3}{5}$. 14. 65. 15. $10\frac{11}{14}$. 16. 2079.
17. $3029\frac{1}{4}$. 18. $4912\frac{1}{2}$. 19. $52401\frac{1}{2}$. 20. $83191\frac{1}{4}$.
21. $11318\frac{3}{4}$. 22. 14742. 23. 2958. 24. $7598\frac{1}{4}$.

78   FRACTIONS

5. What was the cost of 2½ doz. eggs at 20¢ a dozen?

6. What is the cost of 2 yd. of cloth at 12½¢ a yard?

7. A man bought ½ a bushel of seed, and sowed half of it; how much did he sow?

8. There are 5½ yd. in a rod; how many yards are there in ⅓ of a rod?

9. A man owned ½ an acre of land and sold ¾ of it; how much did he sell?

10. What should ⅔ of a yard of silk cost at $3 a yard?

11. ¾ of a foot is how many inches?

12. What will ¾ of a pound of dried beef cost at 32¢ a pound?

13. Find the cost of 8 lb. of coffee at $⅖ a pound.

14. Eight 2½-dollar gold pieces are worth how much?

15. Find the cost of 2½ lb. of sugar at 8¢ a pound.

16. Find the cost of ¾ lb. of spices at 40¢ a pound.

17. Find the cost of 1½ lb. of butter at 30¢ a pound.

18. Find the cost of ½ lb. of tea at 60¢ a pound.

19. How much milk does a family use in a week if it uses 2½ quarts in a day?

Exercise 60

1. When eggs are selling at 30¢ a dozen how much should be paid for 10½ doz.?

2. 16½ ft. make 1 rod; how many feet are there in 12 rods?

vi ANSWERS

25. $2006\frac{2}{3}$. 26. $20317\frac{1}{2}$. 27. $4086\frac{2}{3}$. 28. $4257\frac{4}{5}$.
29. $3118\frac{1}{4}$. 30. $5974\frac{12}{13}$. 31. $17{,}024\frac{1}{13}$. 32. $3683\frac{1}{2}$.
33. $2929\frac{1}{4}$. 34. $23{,}259\frac{8}{10}$. 35. $19{,}860\frac{1}{4}$. 36. $29{,}592\frac{2}{3}$.
37. $15{,}826\frac{1}{4}$. 38. $7957\frac{11}{13}$. 39. $11{,}849\frac{9}{10}$.

Exercise 59, page 77

1. $12\cancel{c}$. 2. $10\frac{1}{2}$. 3. 6 mi. 4. $10\cancel{c}$. 5. $50\cancel{c}$. 6. $25\cancel{c}$.
7. $\frac{1}{2}$ bu. 8. $1\frac{1}{8}$. 9. $\frac{3}{8}$ A. 10. $2. 11. 9. 12. $24\cancel{c}$.
13. $3\frac{1}{8}$. 14. $20. 15. $20\cancel{c}$. 16. $30\cancel{c}$. 17. $45\cancel{c}$. 18. $30\cancel{c}$.
19. $17\frac{1}{2}$ qt.

Exercise 60, page 78

1. $3.15. 2. 198. 3. $207. 4. 875 lb. 5. $31\frac{7}{8}$.
6. $18\frac{3}{4}$. 7. $12\frac{1}{2}$ lb. 8. $5\frac{1}{16}$. 9. $31\frac{1}{4}$ bu. 10. $14\frac{7}{15}$ in.
11. $365. 12. 1375 lb. 13. $585\frac{3}{4}$. 14. $7\frac{7}{8}$.

Exercise 62, page 81

1. $\frac{7}{8}$. 2. $\frac{1}{4}$. 3. $\frac{1}{10}$. 4. $\frac{1}{4}$. 5. $\frac{1}{4}$. 6. $\frac{1}{4}$.
7. $\frac{1}{8}$ A. 8. $\frac{7}{16}$ in. 9. $\frac{8}{15}$ bu. 10. $\frac{1}{15}$. 11. $\frac{7}{8}$ A. 12. $\frac{1}{32}$ lb.

Exercise 67, page 85

1. $\frac{3}{8}$. 2. $1\frac{1}{15}$. 3. $\frac{27}{24}$. 4. $\frac{3}{8}$. 5. $1\frac{1}{4}$. 6. $\frac{15}{16}$. 7. $\frac{17}{44}$.
8. $\frac{8}{15}$. 9. 3. 10. $3\frac{3}{4}$. 11. $9\frac{1}{4}$. 12. 4. 13. 3. 14. $2\frac{4}{7}$.
15. $2\frac{2}{11}$. 16. $\frac{8}{15}$. 17. $1\frac{1}{4}$. 18. $1\frac{10}{11}$. 19. $\frac{1}{4}$. 20. $\frac{20}{21}$. 21. $\frac{1}{4}$.
22. $\frac{1}{4}$. 23. 2. 24. $\frac{1}{4}$. 25. $1\frac{1}{8}$. 26. $2\frac{3}{8}$. 27. 3.

Exercise 68, page 86

1. 7. 2. $1\frac{4}{8}$. 3. 2. 4. 18. 5. $7\frac{1}{2}$. 6. $21\frac{2}{8}$.
7. 14. 8. $6\frac{7}{8}$. 9. $7\frac{1}{4}$. 10. 12.

Exercise 69, page 86

1. 4. 2. 20. 3. 32. 4. 10. 5. $18\frac{1}{4}$. 6. 19.
7. $16\frac{2}{3}$. 8. 20. 9. 4 mi. 10. 25. 11. 2. 12. 96.
13. $18\frac{2}{3}$. 14. 20. 15. 80.

Exercise 70, page 88

1. 6. 2. 3. 3. 12. 4. 8. 5. 12. 6. 18.
7. 10. 8. 60 lb. 9. 25. 10. $36.

80. To divide any number by a fraction, multiply the number by the inverse of the fraction.

81. 1. Divide 4 by $\frac{3}{5}$.

$$4 \div \tfrac{3}{5} = \tfrac{5}{3} \times 4 = \tfrac{20}{3} = 6\tfrac{2}{3}.$$

2. Divide $\frac{4}{5}$ by $\frac{2}{3}$.

$$\frac{4}{5} \div \tfrac{2}{3} = \frac{3}{\underset{}{2}} \times \frac{\overset{2}{4}}{5} = \frac{6}{5} = 1\tfrac{1}{5}.$$

3. Divide $3\frac{1}{3}$ by $2\frac{1}{2}$.

$$3\tfrac{1}{3} \div 2\tfrac{1}{2} = \frac{10}{3} \div \frac{5}{2} = \frac{\overset{2}{10}}{3} \times \frac{2}{\underset{}{5}} = \frac{4}{3} = 1\tfrac{1}{3}.$$

Exercise 67

Find the quotients :

1. $\frac{2}{3} \div \frac{3}{4}$ 2. $\frac{4}{5} \div \frac{3}{4}$ 3. $\frac{6}{7} \div \frac{8}{9}$

4. $\frac{9}{10} \div \frac{3}{2}$ 5. $\frac{15}{16} \div \frac{3}{4}$ 6. $\frac{7}{8} \div \frac{9}{10}$

7. $\frac{9}{16} \div \frac{11}{12}$ 8. $\frac{5}{9} \div \frac{25}{24}$ 9. $2 \div \frac{2}{3}$

10. $3 \div \frac{4}{5}$ 11. $7 \div \frac{3}{4}$ 12. $5 \div \frac{5}{4}$

13. $4 \div 1\frac{1}{3}$ 14. $9 \div 3\frac{1}{2}$ 15. $8 \div 3\frac{2}{3}$

16. $4 \div 7\frac{1}{2}$ 17. $1\frac{1}{2} \div 1\frac{1}{3}$ 18. $3\frac{1}{3} \div 1\frac{3}{4}$

19. $2\frac{1}{2} \div 7\frac{1}{2}$ 20. $3\frac{1}{3} \div 3\frac{1}{2}$ 21. $1\frac{3}{4} \div 5\frac{1}{4}$

22. $1\frac{2}{3} \div 6\frac{2}{3}$ 23. $12\frac{1}{2} \div 6\frac{1}{4}$ 24. $2\frac{6}{7} \div 14\frac{2}{7}$

25. $3 \div 2\frac{2}{3}$ 26. $4 \div 1\frac{1}{2}$ 27. $10 \div 3\frac{1}{3}$

25. $2006\frac{2}{3}$. 26. $20317\frac{1}{2}$. 27. $4086\frac{5}{8}$. 28. $4257\frac{5}{6}$.
29. $3118\frac{1}{6}$. 30. $5974\frac{19}{24}$. 31. $17{,}024\frac{1}{12}$. 32. $3683\frac{1}{6}$.
33. $2929\frac{1}{6}$. 34. $23{,}259\frac{3}{10}$. 35. $19{,}860\frac{3}{4}$. 36. $29{,}592\frac{2}{3}$.
37. $15{,}826\frac{1}{3}$. 38. $7957\frac{11}{12}$. 39. $11{,}849\frac{9}{10}$.

Exercise 59, page 77

1. 12¢. 2. $10\frac{1}{2}$. 3. 6 mi. 4. 10¢. 5. 50¢. 6. 25¢.
7. $\frac{1}{4}$ bu. 8. $1\frac{5}{6}$. 9. $\frac{3}{8}$ A. 10. $2. 11. 9. 12. 24¢.
13. $\$3\frac{1}{3}$. 14. $20. 15. 20¢. 16. 30¢. 17. 45¢. 18. 30¢.
19. $17\frac{1}{2}$ qt.

Exercise 60, page 78

1. $3.15. 2. 198. 3. $207. 4. 875 lb. 5. $31\frac{7}{8}$.
6. $\$18\frac{3}{4}$. 7. $12\frac{1}{2}$ lb. 8. $\$5\frac{1}{16}$. 9. $31\frac{1}{4}$ bu. 10. $14\frac{7}{12}$ in.
11. $365. 12. 1375 lb. 13. $585\frac{3}{4}$. 14. $7\frac{7}{8}$.

Exercise 62, page 81

1. $\$\frac{2}{5}$. 2. $\frac{1}{8}$. 3. $\frac{1}{10}$. 4. $\frac{1}{8}$. 5. $\frac{1}{8}$. 6. $\frac{1}{8}$.
7. $\frac{1}{8}$ A. 8. $\frac{7}{16}$ in. 9. $\frac{3}{16}$ bu. 10. $\frac{1}{16}$. 11. $\frac{7}{8}$ A. 12. $\frac{1}{32}$ lb.

Exercise 67, page 85

1. $\frac{8}{9}$. 2. $1\frac{1}{15}$. 3. $\frac{27}{28}$. 4. $\frac{3}{5}$. 5. $1\frac{1}{4}$. 6. $\frac{35}{36}$. 7. $\frac{27}{44}$.
8. $\frac{8}{15}$. 9. 3. 10. $3\frac{3}{4}$. 11. $9\frac{1}{3}$. 12. 4. 13. 3. 14. $2\frac{4}{7}$.
15. $2\frac{2}{11}$. 16. $\frac{8}{15}$. 17. $1\frac{1}{8}$. 18. $1\frac{19}{21}$. 19. $\frac{1}{3}$. 20. $\frac{20}{21}$. 21. $\frac{1}{3}$.
22. $\frac{1}{4}$. 23. 2. 24. $\frac{1}{5}$. 25. $1\frac{1}{8}$. 26. $2\frac{2}{3}$. 27. 3.

Exercise 68, page 86

1. 7. 2. $1\frac{3}{5}$. 3. 2. 4. 18. 5. $7\frac{1}{2}$. 6. $21\frac{2}{3}$.
7. 14. 8. $6\frac{7}{8}$. 9. $7\frac{1}{3}$. 10. 12.

Exercise 69, page 86

1. 4. 2. 20. 3. 32. 4. 10. 5. $13\frac{1}{3}$. 6. 19.
7. $16\frac{2}{3}$. 8. 20. 9. 4 mi. 10. 25. 11. 2. 12. 96.
13. $13\frac{7}{8}$. 14. 20. 15. 80.

Exercise 70, page 88

1. 6. 2. 3. 3. 12. 4. 8. 5. 12. 6. 18.
7. 10. 8. 60 lb. 9. 25. 10. $36.

3

Decimals

> "I continued to do arithmetic with my father, passing proudly through fractions to decimals. I eventually arrived at the point where so many cows ate so much grass, and tanks filled with water in so many hours I found it quite enthralling. "
> ~ Agatha Christie

Decimal Place Value - Addition

Addition and Subtraction

Multiplication and Division

Decimal Place Value - Addition

Wednesday, December 8, 2021   11:19 PM

Place Value - How the Prime's Home View handles numbers. Prime settings determine the output displayed.

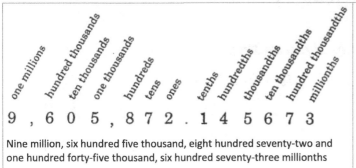

9 , 6 0 5 , 8 7 2 . 1 4 5 6 7 3

Nine million, six hundred five thousand, eight hundred seventy-two and one hundred forty-five thousand, six hundred seventy-three millionths

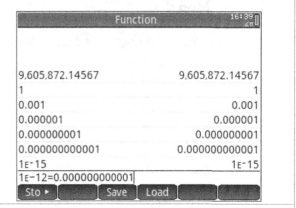

9,605,872.14567	9,605,872.14567
1	1
0.001	0.001
0.000001	0.000001
0.000000001	0.000000001
0.000000000001	0.000000000001
1E-15	1E-15
1E-12=0.000000000001	

Use of E-12 (trillionth), E-9 (billionth), E-6 (millionth) helpful in command line input. E-3 (thousandth) optional. Calculator displays only 12 digits. Use place value calculator to write decimal part in word form.

[Home] Entry of decimal number on left is truncated to twelve digits. Entry of 1, 1E-3, 1E-6, 1E-9, 1E-12, 1E-15 are shown above. Example 0.000001: [1] [EEX] [-6] Note: Last entry displays 1 (True).

For Addition use Home View to display commas. Leave Prime set to default setting for everyday problems.

375.4 + 236.3
84.71 + 83.74
4.732 + 3.645
0.5663 + 0.2349

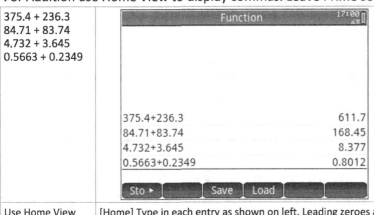

375.4+236.3	611.7
84.71+83.74	168.45
4.732+3.645	8.377
0.5663+0.2349	0.8012

Read aloud the word form of the calculator solution in the two screen's history area.

Read Aloud (word form)
0.8
15.7
197.78
836.432
2,420.6578
40,476.35057

Use Home View calculator.	[Home] Type in each entry as shown on left. Leading zeroes are optional. Following each entry press [Enter].	Calculator keys - [Backspace] deletes keystroke - [Esc] clears command line - [Clear] after [Esc] erases History area.

Exercise 76

Read :

1. .025   Thus, *twenty-five thousandths.*

2. 7.32   Thus, *seven and thirty-two hundredths.*

3. .25	4. .201	5. .42	6. .572
7. .304	8. .27	9. .750	10. .820
11. .09	12. .74	13. .047	14. .274
15. 4.07	16. 8.47	17. 5.704	18. 6.549
19. 7.4	20. 3.742	21. 2.523	22. 9.248

Exercise 77

Write in decimal form :

1. $\frac{25}{100}$	2. $\frac{75}{100}$	3. $\frac{80}{100}$	4. $\frac{50}{100}$
5. $\frac{45}{100}$	6. $\frac{25}{1000}$	7. $\frac{50}{1000}$	8. $\frac{375}{1000}$
9. $\frac{205}{1000}$	10. $\frac{210}{1000}$	11. $\frac{500}{1000}$	12. $\frac{675}{1000}$

13. 24 hundredths.   SUGGESTION. — Write 24 and so place the decimal point that 4 stands in *hundredths'* place; thus, .24.

14. 15 tenths.   SUGGESTION. — Write 15 and so place the decimal point that 5 stands in *tenths'* place; thus, 1.5.

15. 12 hundredths	16. 25 thousandths
17. 16 thousandths	18. 30 thousandths
19. 15 hundredths	20. 50 hundredths
21. 22 hundredths	22. 12 tenths
23. 67 hundredths	24. 132 thousandths

SUBTRACTION   105

Exercise 81

Find the sum of:

1.	2.	3.
6.14	1.004	.403
.186	.31	4.25
31.4	25.06	.117
.561	.9	12.075

4. .6, .074, and .73.

5. 2.19, 7.005, and 15.3.

6. .45, 3.77, .017, and .711.

7. 30.03, 114.250, .09, and .02.

8. 7 tenths, 52 hundredths, and 19 thousandths.

9. 3 and 1 tenth, 21 thousandths, and 3 and 8 hundredths.

10. 4 tenths, 78 hundredths, and 220 thousandths.

11. 13 and 21 thousandths, 6 and 6 hundredths, and 8 tenths.

SUBTRACTION

92. 1. From 12.75 take 7.9.   2. From 28.7 take 1.245.

12.75	28.700
7.9	1.245
4.85	27.455

Write the numbers so that units of the same order stand in the same column, and subtract as in subtraction of whole numbers. Place the decimal point between units and tenths in the difference.

viii   ANSWERS

Exercise 78, page 103

1. .50.   2. .080.   3. .2.   4. .42.   5. .850.   6. .30.   7. .9.
8. .040.   9. .24.   10. .3.   11. .370.   12. .70.   13. .600.   14. .050.
15. .4.   16. .80.   17. .550.   18. .6.

Exercise 79, page 103

2. $\frac{4}{5}$.   3. $\frac{1}{4}$.   4. $7\frac{3}{5}$.   5. $\frac{3}{5}$.   6. $\frac{7}{15}$.   7. $3\frac{3}{4}$.   8. $\frac{1}{4}$.   9. $\frac{5}{8}$.
10. $\frac{7}{8}$.   11. $\frac{5}{8}$.   12. $\frac{1}{2}$.   13. $1\frac{1}{8}$.   14. $\frac{9}{40}$.   15. $7\frac{3}{4}$.   16. $8\frac{1}{2}$.   17. $7\frac{9}{20}$.
18. $9\frac{4}{5}$.   19. $10\frac{9}{30}$.

Exercise 80, page 104

1. .5.   2. .8.   3. .06.   4. .08.   5. .25.   6. .14.   7. .36.
8. .3.   9. .625.   10. .045.   11. .875.   12. .014.   13. .85.   14. .44.
15. 2.9.   16. 8.5.   17. 5.8.   18. 7.12.   19. 8.06.   20. 10.2.

Exercise 81, page 105

1. 38.287.   2. 27.274.   3. 16.845.   4. 1.404.   5. 24.495.   6. 4.948.
7. 144.39.   8. 1.239.   9. 6.201.   10. 1.4.   11. 19.881.

Exercise 82, page 106

1. 4.472.   2. 1.659.   3. 4.3.   4. 3.763.   5. 1.3.   6. 5.53.
7. 50.06.   8. 19.065.   9. 2.569.   10. 2.989.   11. 5.979.   12. 8.514.
13. 8.109.   14. 25.088.   15. .663.   16. 2.85.   17. .709.   18. 9.44.

Exercise 83, page 106

1. $350.46.   2. $11.75.   3. $189.33.   5. $33.17.   6. 8.4 ft.   7. 6.05.
8. $5.   9. $113.04.   10. 18 ft.

Exercise 84, page 109

1. .88.   2. 131.84.   3. 51.2.   4. 2.925.   5. 346.551.   6. 15.04.
7. .66.   8. 2.24.   9. 1.684.   10. 19.17.   11. 4.41.   12. .351.
13. 59.878.   14. 25.19.   15. 529.   16. 9.342.   17. 275.2.
18. 103.092.   19. 1131.6.   20. 51.36.   21. 194.06.   22. 234.9.   23. 141.52.
24. 33.28.   25. 2912.   26. 109.9.

Exercise 86, page 111

1. .001.   2. .4.   3. .09.   4. .09.   5. .004.   6. .002.
7. 1.02;   8. .04.   9. .005.   10. .0005.   11. .001.   12. 1.002.
13. .9.   14. .25.   15. .015.   16. .25.   17. .016.   18. .12.
19. .06.   20. .06.   21. .015.   22. .14.   23. .025.   24. .036.

Subtraction

Wednesday, December 8, 2021   11:50 PM

For Subtraction use Home View to display commas. Leave Prime set to default setting for everyday problems.

632.1 − 546.8		
65.34 − 39.85		
6.905 − 2.907		
0.8408 − 0.4686		

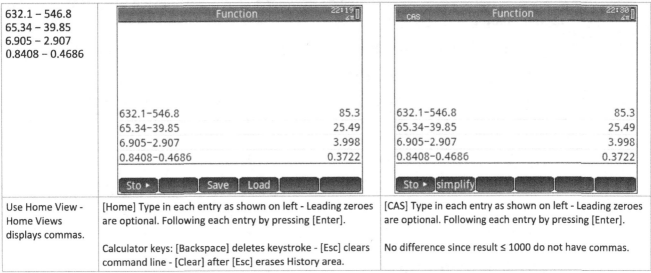

Function 22:19		CAS Function 22:30	
632.1−546.8	85.3	632.1−546.8	85.3
65.34−39.85	25.49	65.34−39.85	25.49
6.905−2.907	3.998	6.905−2.907	3.998
0.8408−0.4686	0.3722	0.8408−0.4686	0.3722
Sto ▶ Save Load		Sto ▶ simplify	

Use Home View - Home Views displays commas.	[Home] Type in each entry as shown on left - Leading zeroes are optional. Following each entry by pressing [Enter]. Calculator keys: [Backspace] deletes keystroke - [Esc] clears command line - [Clear] after [Esc] erases History area.	[CAS] Type in each entry as shown on left - Leading zeroes are optional. Following each entry by pressing [Enter]. No difference since result ≤ 1000 do not have commas.

What is the area of Greater New York? Greater New York is composed of the following boroughs, with the area of each given as Manhattan 21.93 sq mi, Brooklyn 77.62 sq mi, The Bronx 40.65 sq mi, Queens 129.50 sq mi, and Staten Island 57.19 sq mi.

How much larger is Brooklyn than The Bronx? How much larger is Staten Island than Manhattan?

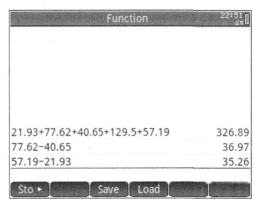

Function 22:51	
21.93+77.62+40.65+129.5+57.19	326.89
77.62−40.65	36.97
57.19−21.93	35.26
Sto ▶ Save Load	

[Home} Type in entry as shown. Press [Enter]

106 DECIMALS

Exercise 82

Subtract:

1.	2.	3.	4.
5.632	4.000	7.4	8.
1.16	2.341	3.100	4.237

5.	6.	7.	8.
2.40	6.10	52.1	32.07
1.10	.57	2.04	13.005

Find the difference:

9. $3 - .431$ 10. $3 - .011$

11. $6.101 - .122$ 12. $8.52 - .006$

13. $8.13 - .021$ 14. $25.2 - .112$

Find the difference between:

15. 72 hundredths and 57 thousandths.

16. 3 and 4 tenths and 55 hundredths.

17. 73 hundredths and 21 thousandths.

18. 9 and 8 tenths and 36 hundredths.

Problems

Exercise 83

1. A merchant had $172.40 cash on hand at the beginning of a day. During the day he received $264.18 and paid out $86.12. What was his cash balance at the close of the day?

viii ANSWERS

Exercise 78, page 103

1. .50. 2. .080. 3. .2. 4. .42. 5. .850. 6. .30. 7. .9.
8. .040. 9. .24. 10. .3. 11. .370. 12. .70. 13. .600. 14. .050.
15. .4. 16. .80. 17. .550. 18. .6.

Exercise 79, page 103

2. $\frac{4}{5}$. 3. $\frac{1}{4}$. 4. $7\frac{2}{3}$. 5. $\frac{2}{3}$. 6. $\frac{1}{25}$. 7. $3\frac{3}{4}$. 8. $\frac{1}{4}$. 9. $\frac{1}{5}$.
10. $\frac{7}{8}$. 11. $\frac{1}{8}$. 12. $\frac{1}{2}$. 13. $1\frac{1}{8}$. 14. $\frac{9}{40}$. 15. $7\frac{3}{4}$. 16. $8\frac{1}{2}$. 17. $7\frac{9}{20}$.
18. $9\frac{4}{5}$. 19. $10\frac{9}{10}$.

Exercise 80, page 104

1. .5. 2. .8. 3. .06. 4. .08. 5. .25. 6. .14. 7. .36.
8. .3. 9. .625. 10. .045. 11. .875. 12. .014. 13. .85. 14. .44.
15. 2.9. 16. 8.5. 17. 5.8. 18. 7.12. 19. 8.06. 20. 10.2.

Exercise 81, page 105

1. 38.287. 2. 27.274. 3. 16.845. 4. 1.404. 5. 24.495. 6. 4.948.
7. 144.39. 8. 1.239. 9. 6.201. 10. 1.4. 11. 19.881.

Exercise 82, page 106

1. 4.472. 2. 1.659. 3. 4.3. 4. 3.763. 5. 1.3. 6. 5.53.
7. 50.06. 8. 19.065. 9. 2.569. 10. 2.989. 11. 5.979. 12. 8.514.
13. 8.109. 14. 25.088. 15. .663. 16. 2.85. 17. .709. 18. 9.44.

Exercise 83, page 106

1. $350.46. 2. $11.75. 3. $189.33. 5. $33.17. 6. 8.4 ft. 7. 6.05.
8. $5. 9. $113.04. 10. 18 ft.

Exercise 84, page 109

1. .88. 2. 131.84. 3. 51.2. 4. 2.925. 5. 346.551. 6. 15.04.
7. .66. 8. 2.24. 9. 1.684. 10. 19.17. 11. 4.41. 12. .351.
13. 59.878. 14. 25.19. 15. 529. 16. 9.342. 17. 275.2.
18. 103.092. 19. 1131.6. 20. 51.36. 21. 194.06. 22. 234.9. 23. 141.52.
24. 33.28. 25. 2912. 26. 109.9.

Exercise 86, page 111

1. .001. 2. .4. 3. .09. 4. .09. 5. .004. 6. .002.
7. 1.02; 8. .04. 9. .005. 10. .0005. 11. .001. 12. 1.002.
13. .9. 14. .25. 15. .015. 16. .25. 17. .016. 18. .12.
19. .06. 20. .06. 21. .015. 22. .14. 23. .025. 24. .036.

Multiplication and Division

Thursday, December 9, 2021   10:50 AM

For Prime multiplication and division use Home View to display commas. Default settings for everyday problems.

MULTIPLY AND DIVIDE 1,145 *by* 2.2	Function 01:45	
0.375 *by* 0.0004	1.145*2.2	2.519
	0.375*0.0004	0.00015
95.1 *by* 3,000	9.51*3,000	28,530
	0.2589*8.92	2.309388
0.2589 *by* 8.92		415,803
		$\frac{180,049}{}$
		$2+\frac{55,705}{180,049}$

Function 00:06	
$\frac{1,145}{2.2}$	520.454545455
	$520+\frac{5}{11}$
$\frac{0.375}{0.0004}$	937.5
$\frac{95.1}{3,000}$	0.0317
$\frac{0.2589}{8.92}$	2.90246636771E^-2

| Use Home View - Home Views [a b/c] key toggles History area display of the problem result. | [Home] Type in each entry as multiplication. Press [Enter] following each entry.

Pressed [Enter] three times and toggled result for last entry. | [Home] Type in each entry as division. Press [Enter] following each entry.

Pressed [Enter] two times and toggled result for first entry. |

For the ROUND command - press [Toolbox] - if necessary select soft key [Catlg] - letter R (8 key) and scroll.

FINDING THE QUOTIENT APPROXIMATELY

When the division does not terminate, it is seldom carried in practice beyond the fifth decimal place in the quotient, which is usually expressed to the nearest ten thousandth 0.0001. Primes uses a 4 for ten thousandth as its second parameter in the ROUND command.

LONG DIVISION

$$.21142^+ = .2114, \text{ correct to the nearest } .0001.$$
$$35)\overline{7.40000}$$

7 0
$\overline{40}$
35
$\overline{\text{etc.}}$

NOTE. If the quotient were .21146,⁺ expressed to the nearest .0001, it would be .2115.

Function 01:13	
$\frac{1,145}{2.2}$	520.454545455
ROUND(520.454545455,4)	520.4545
$\frac{0.2589}{8.92}$	2.90246636771E^-2
ROUND(2.90246636771E^-2,4)	0.029
ROUND(2.90246636771E^-2,5)	0.02902
ROUND$\left(\frac{7.4}{35},4\right)$	0.2114

[Home} Type in entries. Used copied as well. Press [Enter] following each entry. Prime drops unnecessary zeroes.

MULTIPLICATION 109

Multiply .065 by 35; .065 by 420.

In practice find the products thus:

```
  .065              .065
   35               420
  ───               ─────
  325              1 300
1 95               26 0
 ────              ──────
2.275             27.300
```

Exercise 84

Multiply:

1. .22
   4

2. 4.12
   32

3. 1.28
   40

4. .117
   25

5. 1.627
   213

6. .047
   320

7. .22 by 3

8. .56 by 4

9. .421 by 4

10. 2.13 by 9

11. .63 by 7

12. .117 by 3

13. 4.606 by 13

14. 1.145 by 22

15. 21.16 by 25

16. .173 by 54

17. 8.60 by 32

18. 3.124 by 33

19. 9.20 by 123

20. .16 by 321

21. .313 by 620

22. 2.175 by 108

23. 1.220 by 116

24. .104 by 320

25. 14.56 by 200

26. .785 by 140

viii ANSWERS

Exercise 78, page 103

1. .50. 2. .080. 3. .2. 4. .42. 5. .850. 6. .30. 7. .9.
8. .040. 9. .24. 10. .3. 11. .370. 12. .70. 13. .600. 14. .050.
15. .4. 16. .80. 17. .550. 18. .6.

Exercise 79, page 103

2. $\frac{4}{5}$. 3. $\frac{1}{4}$. 4. $7\frac{1}{2}$. 5. $\frac{3}{5}$. 6. $\frac{7}{25}$. 7. $3\frac{1}{4}$. 8. $\frac{1}{4}$. 9. $\frac{5}{8}$.
10. $\frac{7}{8}$. 11. $\frac{5}{8}$. 12. $\frac{1}{2}$. 13. $1\frac{1}{8}$. 14. $\frac{9}{40}$. 15. $7\frac{1}{4}$. 16. $8\frac{1}{2}$. 17. $7\frac{9}{25}$.
18. $9\frac{4}{5}$. 19. $10\frac{9}{40}$.

Exercise 80, page 104

1. .5. 2. .8. 3. .06. 4. .08. 5. .25. 6. .14. 7. .36.
8. .3. 9. .625. 10. .045. 11. .875. 12. .014. 13. .85. 14. .44.
15. 2.9. 16. 8.5. 17. 5.8. 18. 7.12. 19. 8.06. 20. 10.2.

Exercise 81, page 105

1. 38.287. 2. 27.274. 3. 16.845. 4. 1.404. 5. 24.495. 6. 4.948.
7. 144.39. 8. 1.239. 9. 6.201. 10. 1.4. 11. 19.881.

Exercise 82, page 106

1. 4.472. 2. 1.659. 3. 4.3. 4. 3.763. 5. 1.3. 6. 5.53.
7. 50.06. 8. 19.065. 9. 2.569. 10. 2.989. 11. 5.979. 12. 8.514.
13. 8.109. 14. 25.088. 15. .663. 16. 2.85. 17. .709. 18. 9.44.

Exercise 83, page 106

1. $350.46. 2. $11.75. 3. $189.33. 5. $33.17. 6. 8.4 ft. 7. 6.05.
8. $5. 9. $113.04. 10. 18 ft.

Exercise 84, page 109

1. .88. 2. 131.84. 3. 51.2. 4. 2.925. 5. 346.551. 6. 15.04.
7. .66. 8. 2.24. 9. 1.684. 10. 19.17. 11. 4.41. 12. .351.
13. 59.878. 14. 25.19. 15. 529. 16. 9.342. 17. 275.2.
18. 103.092. 19. 1131.6. 20. 51.36. 21. 194.06. 22. 234.9. 23. 141.52.
24. 83.28. 25. 2912. 26. 109.9.

Exercise 86, page 111

1. .001. 2. .4. 3. .09. 4. .09. 5. .004. 6. .002.
7. 1.02; 8. .04. 9. .005. 10. .0005. 11. .001. 12. 1.002.
13. .9. 14. .25. 15. .015. 16. .25. 17. .016. 18. .12.
19. .06. 20. .06. 21. .015. 22. .14. 23. .025. 24. .036.

112 DECIMALS

16. 3.5 by 14   17. .256 by 16   18. 5.4 by 45

19. 2.52 by 42   20. 1.5 by 25   21. .27 by 18

22. 5.32 by 38   23. .875 by 35   24. 1.512 by 42

Dividing Decimals by 10, 100, and 1000

97. 1. $.04 \div 10 = \frac{4}{100} \div 10 = \frac{4}{1000}$, or .004

2. $.4 \div 100 = \frac{4}{10} \div 100 = \frac{4}{1000}$, or .004

3. $4 \div 1000 = \frac{4}{1000}$, or .004

In 1, 2, and 3 observe the position of the decimal points in the dividend and in the quotient.

Moving the decimal point one place to the left divides by 10, moving it two places to the left divides by 100, moving it three places to the left divides by 1000.

Exercise 87

Read, supplying at sight the missing quotients:

1. $5 \div 10$ Thus, $5 \div 10 = .5$

2. $25 \div 100$ Thus, $25 \div 100 = .25$

3. $36 \div 1000$ Thus, $36 \div 1000 = .036$

4. $6 \div 10$ 5. $50 \div 10$

6. $15 \div 10$ 7. $.3 \div 10$

8. $.5 \div 10$ 9. $2.5 \div 10$

10. $1.2 \div 10$ 11. $.02 \div 10$

12. $.75 \div 10$ 13. $.82 \div 10$

14. $.07 \div 10$ 15. $.32 \div 10$

16. $7 \div 100$ 17. $1 \div 100$

112   **DECIMALS**

16. 3.5 by 14   17. .256 by 16   18. 5.4 by 45
19. 2.52 by 42   20. 1.5 by 25   21. .27 by 18
22. 5.32 by 38   23. .875 by 35   24. 1.512 by 42

Dividing Decimals by 10, 100, and 1000

97. 1. $.04 \div 10 = \frac{4}{100} \div 10 = \frac{4}{1000}$, or .004

2. $.4 \div 100 = \frac{4}{10} \div 100 = \frac{4}{1000}$, or .004

3. $4 \div 1000 = \frac{4}{1000}$, or .004

In 1, 2, and 3 observe the position of the decimal points in the dividend and in the quotient.

Moving the decimal point one place to the left divides by 10, moving it two places to the left divides by 100, moving it three places to the left divides by 1000.

Exercise 87

Read, supplying at sight the missing quotients:

1. $5 \div 10$ Thus, $5 \div 10 = .5$

2. $25 \div 100$ Thus, $25 \div 100 = .25$

3. $36 \div 1000$ Thus, $36 \div 1000 = .036$

4. $6 \div 10$ 5. $50 \div 10$

6. $15 \div 10$ 7. $.3 \div 10$

8. $.5 \div 10$ 9. $2.5 \div 10$

10. $1.2 \div 10$ 11. $.02 \div 10$

12. $.75 \div 10$ 13. $.82 \div 10$

14. $.07 \div 10$ 15. $.32 \div 10$

16. $7 \div 100$ 17. $1 \div 100$

viii ANSWERS

Exercise 78, page 103

1. .50.   2. .080.   3. .2.   4. .42.   5. .850.   6. .30.   7. .9.
8. .040.   9. .24.   10. .3.   11. .370.   12. .70.   13. .600.   14. .050.
15. .4.   16. .80.   17. .550.   18. .6.

Exercise 79, page 103

2. $\frac{4}{5}$.   3. $\frac{1}{4}$.   4. $7\frac{3}{4}$.   5. $\frac{2}{3}$.   6. $\frac{1}{15}$.   7. $3\frac{1}{2}$.   8. $\frac{1}{4}$.   9. $\frac{5}{8}$.
10. $\frac{7}{8}$.   11. $\frac{3}{8}$.   12. $\frac{1}{4}$.   13. $1\frac{1}{4}$.   14. $\frac{9}{10}$.   15. $7\frac{1}{4}$.   16. $8\frac{1}{2}$.   17. $7\frac{9}{20}$.
18. $9\frac{4}{5}$.   19. $10\frac{9}{20}$.

Exercise 80, page 104

1. .5.   2. .8.   3. .06.   4. .08.   5. .25.   6. .14.   7. .36.
8. .3.   9. .625.   10. .045.   11. .875.   12. .014.   13. .85.   14. .44.
15. 2.9.   16. 8.5.   17. 5.8.   18. 7.12.   19. 8.06.   20. 10.2.

Exercise 81, page 105

1. 38.287.   2. 27.274.   3. 16.845.   4. 1.404.   5. 24.495.   6. 4.948.
7. 144.39.   8. 1.239.   9. 6.201.   10. 1.4.   11. 19.881.

Exercise 82, page 106

1. 4.472.   2. 1.659.   3. 4.3.   4. 3.763.   5. 1.3.   6. 5.53.
7. 50.06.   8. 19.065.   9. 2.569.   10. 2.989.   11. 5.979.   12. 8.514.
13. 8.109.   14. 25.088.   15. .663.   16. 2.85.   17. .709.   18. 9.44.

Exercise 83, page 106

1. $350.46.   2. $11.75.   3. $189.33.   5. $33.17.   6. 8.4 ft.   7. 6.05.
8. $5.   9. $113.04.   10. 18 ft.

Exercise 84, page 109

1. .88.   2. 131.84.   3. 51.2.   4. 2.925.   5. 346.551.   6. 15.04.
7. .66.   8. 2.24.   9. 1.684.   10. 19.17.   11. 4.41.   12. .351.
13. 59.878.   14. 25.19.   15. 529.   16. 9.342.   17. 275.2.
18. 103.092.   19. 1131.6.   20. 51.36.   21. 194.06.   22. 234.9.   23. 141.52.
24. 33.28.   25. 2912.   26. 109.9.

Exercise 86, page 111

1. .001.   2. .4.   3. .09.   4. .09.   5. .004.   6. .002.
7. 1.02;   8. .04.   9. .005.   10. .0005.   11. .001.   12. 1.002.
13. .9.   14. .25.   15. .015.   16. .25.   17. .016.   18. .12.
19. .06.   20. .06.   21. .015.   22. .14.   23. .025.   24. .036.

4

Denominate Measurements

"Just because we can't find a solution it
doesn't mean that there isn't one."
~ Andrew Wiles

Prime's Convert Command – CONVERT and abbreviated

Capacity - Volume

Weight – Mass

Time

Length

Surfaces = Area

Solids - Volume

Prime's Convert Command - CONVERT and abbreviated

Thursday, December 9, 2021 8:44 AM

For the CONVERT command - press [Units] physical key - if necessary select soft key [Tools] - select CONVERT - soft key [OK]. Follow steps for abbreviated form given below, except for touch Sto ▸ insert a [,] and type [1].

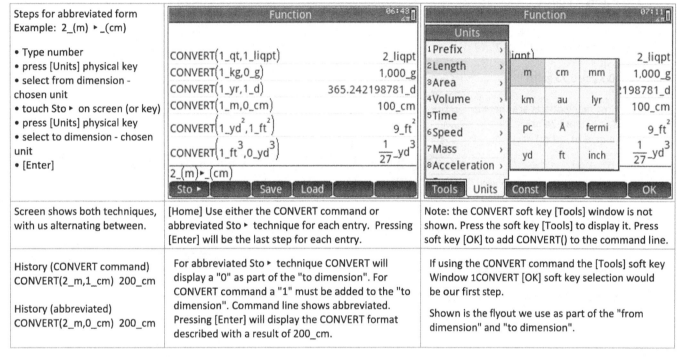

Steps for abbreviated form Example: 2_(m) ▸ _(cm) • Type number • press [Units] physical key • select from dimension - chosen unit • touch Sto ▸ on screen (or key) • press [Units] physical key • select to dimension - chosen unit • [Enter]	[Home] Use either the CONVERT command or abbreviated Sto ▸ technique for each entry. Pressing [Enter] will be the last step for each entry.	Note: the CONVERT soft key [Tools] window is not shown. Press the soft key [Tools] to display it. Press soft key [OK] to add CONVERT() to the command line.
Screen shows both techniques, with us alternating between.	[Home] Use either the CONVERT command or abbreviated Sto ▸ technique for each entry. Pressing [Enter] will be the last step for each entry.	Note: the CONVERT soft key [Tools] window is not shown. Press the soft key [Tools] to display it. Press soft key [OK] to add CONVERT() to the command line.
History (CONVERT command) CONVERT(2_m,1_cm) 200_cm History (abbreviated) CONVERT(2_m,0_cm) 200_cm	For abbreviated Sto ▸ technique CONVERT will display a "0" as part of the "to dimension". For CONVERT command a "1" must be added to the "to dimension". Command line shows abbreviated. Pressing [Enter] will display the CONVERT format described with a result of 200_cm.	If using the CONVERT command the [Tools] soft key Window 1CONVERT [OK] soft key selection would be our first step. Shown is the flyout we use as part of the "from dimension" and "to dimension".

Optional check is to use the Convert units webpage measurements drop down menus to convert one unit to another.

Capacity - Volume

Thursday, December 23, 2021   2:44 PM

MEASURES OF CAPACITY

Liquid Measure 2 pints = 1 quart 4 quarts = 1 gallon What part of a gallon is 2 qt ? 3 qt ? (0.5 gal, 0.75 gal) How many quarts are there in 8 pt? 18 pt? 24 pt? (4 qt, 9 qt, 12 qt)	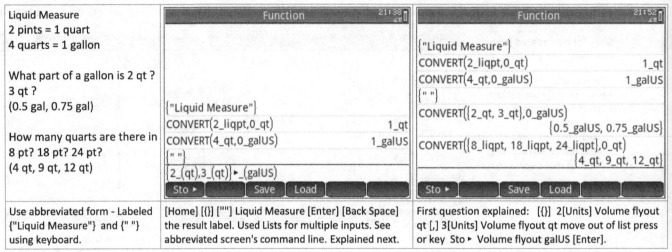
Use abbreviated form - Labeled {"Liquid Measure"} and {" "} using keyboard.	[Home] [{}] [""] Liquid Measure [Enter] [Back Space] the result label. Used Lists for multiple inputs. See abbreviated screen's command line. Explained next.	First question explained: [{}] 2[Units] Volume flyout qt [,] 3[Units] Volume flyout qt move out of list press or key Sto ▸ Volume flyout galUS [Enter].

COMPOUND DENOMINATE MEASURES

Express 3 gal 2 qt 1 pt as pints.

(3 gal = 24 pts, 3 qt = 4 pts, 1pt - Total 29 pts)

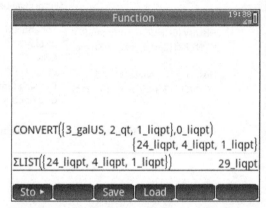

To get the ∑List() command, used in the next screen, press [Toolbox], if necessary soft key [Catlg], scroll the "L's" to select, press soft key [OK].

[Home] Use abbreviated CONVERT as explained in top right screen substituting our new parameters. Get the ∑List() command. Copy list. Press [Enter].

Optional check is to use the Convert units webpage volume's drop down to convert one unit to another unit.

DENOMINATE AMOUNTS

113. Denominate units are units established by custom or law to measure capacity, weight, time, length, surface, solids, etc.

Thus, *a gallon, a pound, a day, a yard,* etc., are denominate units.

114. A simple denominate amount is any number of like denominate units.

Thus, 6 *bushels,* ½ of *a yard,* and 2½ *pounds* are simple denominate amounts.

MEASURES OF CAPACITY

Liquid Measure

115. **Table**

4 gills (gi.)	= 1 pint (pt.)
2 pints	= 1 quart (qt.)
4 quarts	= 1 gallon (gal.)
31½ gallons	= 1 barrel (bbl.)
63 gallons	= 1 hogshead (hhd.)

Barrels are of various sizes, but 31½ gal. is usually taken as the capacity of a barrel unless otherwise stated.

Exercise 93

1. How many pints are there in 4 qt.?
2. One pint is what part of a quart?
3. How many quarts are there in ½ gal.?
4. How many quarts are there in 2½ gal.?
5. How many pints are there in a gallon?

126 DENOMINATE AMOUNTS

6. How many gills are there in a quart?

7. ½ gal. of alcohol will fill how many gill bottles?

8. What part of a gallon is 2 qt.? 3 qt.?

9. How many quarts are there in 8 pt.? 18 pt.? 24 pt.?

10. How many gallons are there in 24 qt.? 32 qt.? 40 qt.?

11. How many gallons are there in 6 qt.? 10 qt.? 15 qt.? 25 qt.?

Dry Measure

116. Table

2 pints (pt.)	= 1 quart (qt.)
8 quarts	= 1 peck (pk.)
4 pecks	= 1 bushel (bu.)

The heaped bushel, which contains about 5 pk., or ⅝ of a stricken bushel, is used in measuring corn in the ear, potatoes, apples, lime, turnips, and various other substances.

Two bushels of corn in the ear are considered the equivalent of one bushel of shelled corn.

Exercise 94

1. How many quarts are there in 3 pk.?

2. A quart is what part of a peck?

3. How many quarts are there in ½ pk.? ¼ pk.?

4. How many quarts are there in a bushel? ½ bu.?

5. One peck is what part of a bushel?

6. Two pecks are what part of a bushel? 3 pk.?

ANSWERS

ix

Exercise 88, page 113

1. .13.   2. .2.   3. .02.   4. .005.   5. .002.   6. .7.
7. .06.   8. .05.   9. .005.   10. .09.   11. .92.   12. .031.
13. .14.   14. 1.2.   15. .024.   16. .12.   17. .15.   18. .025.
19. .12.   20. .24.   21. .25.   22. .5.   23. .5.   24. .75.

Exercise 89, page 114

1. $3125.   2. 141.75 lb.   3. 375 bu.   4. 1250 lb.   5. $0.25.
6. 3.5.   7. 58.5 lb.   8. $1.25.   9. $1.25.   10. $2.50.
11. $4.50.   12. $12.50.   13. $12.50.   14. $19.50.   15. $75.
16. $0.96.   17. $0.288.   18. $56.25.   19. $108.   20. $0.98.
21. $7.   22. $91.

Exercise 91, page 117

1. 96.   2. 12.   3. 84.   4. 75¢.   5. 30¢.   6. 720.
7. $4.96.   8. 60¢.   9. 90 yr.   10. 3.   11. $4.80.   12. $4.
13. $3.   14. 24 lb.   15. $1.60.   16. 30¢.   17. $16.   18. $1.20.
19. $6.   20. $6.25.   21. 12¢.   22. $1.40.   23. $50.

Exercise 92, page 121

1. $20.74.   2. $1.20.   3. $4.25.   4. $3.50.   5. $8.095.
6. $7.455.   7. $212.59.   8. $9.325.   9. $55.   10. $10.78.
11. $12.40.   12. $6.20.   13. $208.60.

Exercise 93, page 125

1. 8.   2. $\frac{1}{2}$.   3. 2.   4. 10.   5. 8.
6. 8.   7. 16.   8. $\frac{1}{2}$; $\frac{1}{4}$.   9. 4; 9; 12.   10. 6; 8; 10.
11. $1\frac{1}{2}$; $2\frac{1}{2}$; $3\frac{3}{4}$; $6\frac{1}{4}$.

Exercise 94, page 126

1. 24.   2. $\frac{1}{3}$.   3. 4; 2.   4. 32; 16.   5. $\frac{1}{4}$.   6. $\frac{1}{2}$; $\frac{3}{4}$.
7. 48.   8. 6.   9. 16.   10. $3.   11. $25.   12. $1.20.
13. 6; 1.   14. 64.

Exercise 95, page 128

1. 28 lb.   2. 15 lb.   3. 4 lb.   4. 5.   5. $22\frac{1}{2}$ lb.   6. 4¢.
7. 240.   8. $9.   9. 10.   10. 12 lb.   11. 5.   12. 20¢.
13. 42¢.

Weight - Mass

Thursday, December 9, 2021   8:47 AM

MEASURES OF WEIGHT - MASS (weight is on earth, mass is anywhere)

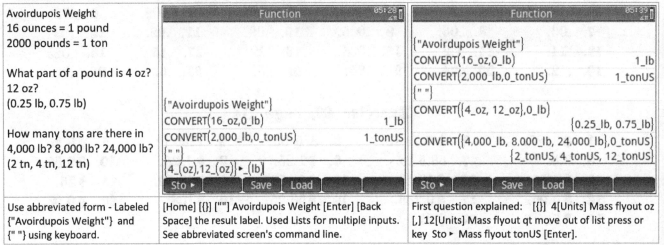

| Avoirdupois Weight
16 ounces = 1 pound
2000 pounds = 1 ton

What part of a pound is 4 oz?
12 oz?
(0.25 lb, 0.75 lb)

How many tons are there in
4,000 lb? 8,000 lb? 24,000 lb?
(2 tn, 4 tn, 12 tn) | Function   05:28
{"Avoirdupois Weight"}
CONVERT(16_oz,0_lb)   1_lb
CONVERT(2,000_lb,0_tonUS)   1_tonUS
{" "}
{4_(oz),12_(oz)}▸_(lb)
Sto ▸   Save   Load | Function   05:39
{"Avoirdupois Weight"}
CONVERT(16_oz,0_lb)   1_lb
CONVERT(2,000_lb,0_tonUS)   1_tonUS
{" "}
CONVERT({4_oz, 12_oz},0_lb)
                        {0.25_lb, 0.75_lb}
CONVERT({4,000_lb, 8,000_lb, 24,000_lb},0_tonUS)
                 {2_tonUS, 4_tonUS, 12_tonUS}
Sto ▸   Save   Load |
| Use abbreviated form - Labeled
{"Avoirdupois Weight"} and
{" "} using keyboard. | [Home] [{}] [""] Avoirdupois Weight [Enter] [Back
Space] the result label. Used Lists for multiple inputs.
See abbreviated screen's command line. | First question explained: [{}] 4[Units] Mass flyout oz
[,] 12[Units] Mass flyout qt move out of list press or
key Sto ▸ Mass flyout tonUS [Enter]. |

COMPOUND DENOMINATE MEASURES

Express 3 lb 12 oz as ounces.

(3 lb = 48 oz, 12 oz - Total 60 oz)

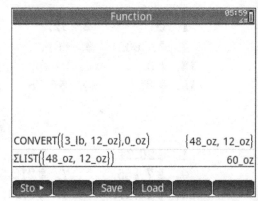

To get the ∑List() command, used in the next screen, press [Toolbox], if necessary soft key [Catlg], scroll the "L's" to select, press soft key [OK].

[Home] Use abbreviated CONVERT as explained in top right screen substituting our new parameters. Get the ∑List() command. Copy list. Press [Enter].

Optional check is to use the Convert units webpage mass' drop down to convert one unit to another unit.

7. How many quarts are there in 1½ bu.?

8. How many half bushels will fill a 3-bu. bag?

9. A trucker put ½ bu. of berries into quart boxes; how many boxes were required?

10. When clover seed sells for $12 per bushel, how much is that per peck?

11. Find the cost of 2½ bu. of clover seed at $10 per bushel.

12. When potatoes are selling at 30¢ a peck, how much is that per bushel?

13. How many bushel sacks will hold 25 pk. of seed, and how many pecks over?

14. How many quart boxes will be required to hold 2 bu. of cherries?

MEASURES OF WEIGHT

Avoirdupois Weight

117. Table

16 ounces (oz.)	**= 1 pound (lb.)**
2000 pounds	**= 1 ton (T.)**

100 lb. is sometimes called 1 *hundredweight* (cwt.). Goods are frequently shipped by the hundredweight.

The long ton, 2240 pounds, is used in custom houses and sometimes elsewhere, especially in selling coal. Anthracite coal is always sold at the mines, and often retailed, by the long ton. Bituminous coal is frequently sold in the same way.

4. How many bushels of bran should there be in 100 lb.?

5. What should $\frac{1}{2}$ bu. of timothy seed weigh?

6. What should 4 oz. of cheese cost at 16¢ per pound?

7. How many more pounds are there in a long ton than in a short ton?

8. What should 1000 lb. of hay cost at $18 per ton?

9. How many 200-lb. sacks of fertilizer will make a ton?

10. How much should a peck of barley weigh?

11. How many bales of hay, each weighing 4 hundredweight, will make a ton?

12. What will $\frac{1}{4}$ lb. of spices cost at 5¢ an ounce?

13. What will 1 lb. 12 oz. of dried beef cost at 24¢ per pound?

120. Find the cost of 4500 lb. of hay at $18.50 per ton.

$$4500 \text{ lb.} = 4.500 \text{ M lb.} = 2.25 \text{ T.}$$
$$\$18.50 = \text{the cost per T.}$$

$$
\begin{array}{r}
2.25 \\
\hline
92\,50 \\
370\,0 \\
3700 \\
\hline
41.6250, \text{ or } \$41.63 = \text{the entire cost.}
\end{array}
$$

Exercise 96

Find the cost of:

1. 1870 lb. of bran at $18 per ton.

2. 3880 lb. of straw at $6 per ton.

3. 4660 lb. of fertilizer at $14 per ton.

ANSWERS

Exercise 88, page 113

1. .13.   2. .2.   3. .02.   4. .005.   5. .002.   6. .7.
7. .06.   8. .05.   9. .005.   10. .09.   11. .92.   12. .031.
13. .14.   14. 1.2.   15. .024.   16. .12.   17. .15.   18. .025.
19. .12.   20. .24.   21. .25.   22. .5.   23. .5.   24. .75.

Exercise 89, page 114

1. $3125.   2. 141.75 lb.   3. 375 bu.   4. 1250 lb.   5. $0.25.
6. 3.5.   7. 58.5 lb.   8. $1.25.   9. $1.25.   10. $2.50.
11. $4.50.   12. $12.50.   13. $12.50.   14. $19.50.   15. $75.
16. $0.96.   17. $0.288.   18. $56.25.   19. $108.   20. $0.98.
21. $7.   22. $91.

Exercise 91, page 117

1. 96.   2. 12.   3. 84.   4. 75¢.   5. 30¢.   6. 720.
7. $4.96.   8. 60¢.   9. 90 yr.   10. 3.   11. $4.80.   12. $4.
13. $3.   14. 24 lb.   15. $1.60.   16. 30¢.   17. $16.   18. $1.20.
19. $6.   20. $6.25.   21. 12¢.   22. $1.40.   23. $50.

Exercise 92, page 121

1. $20.74.   2. $1.20.   3. $4.25.   4. $3.50.   5. $8.095.
6. $7.455.   7. $212.59.   8. $9.325.   9. $55.   10. $10.78.
11. $12.40.   12. $6.20.   13. $208.60.

Exercise 93, page 125

1. 8.   2. $\frac{1}{2}$.   3. 2.   4. 10.   5. 8.
6. 8.   7. 16.   8. $\frac{1}{2}$; $\frac{1}{4}$.   9. 4; 9; 12.   10. 6; 8; 10.
11. $1\frac{1}{2}$; $2\frac{1}{2}$; $3\frac{3}{4}$; $6\frac{1}{4}$.

Exercise 94, page 126

1. 24.   2. $\frac{1}{8}$.   3. 4; 2.   4. 32; 16.   5. $\frac{1}{4}$.   6. $\frac{1}{2}$; $\frac{3}{4}$.
7. 48.   8. 6.   9. 16.   10. $3.   11. $25.   12. $1.20.
13. 6; 1.   14. 64.

Exercise 95, page 128

1. 28 lb.   2. 15 lb.   3. 4 lb.   4. 5.   5. $22\frac{1}{2}$ lb.   6. 4¢.
7. 240.   8. $9.   9. 10.   10. 12 lb.   11. 5.   12. 20¢.
13. 42¢.

Time

Thursday, December 9, 2021   8:48 AM

MEASURES OF TIME

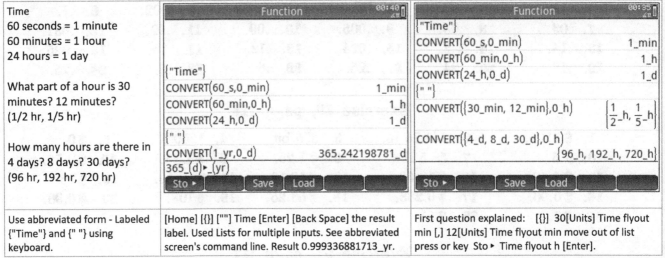

Time 60 seconds = 1 minute 60 minutes = 1 hour 24 hours = 1 day What part of a hour is 30 minutes? 12 minutes? (1/2 hr, 1/5 hr) How many hours are there in 4 days? 8 days? 30 days? (96 hr, 192 hr, 720 hr)	
Use abbreviated form - Labeled {"Time"} and {" "} using keyboard.	[Home] [{}] [""] Time [Enter] [Back Space] the result label. Used Lists for multiple inputs. See abbreviated screen's command line. Result 0.999336881713_yr.

First question explained: [{}] 30[Units] Time flyout min [,] 12[Units] Time flyout min move out of list press or key Sto ▸ Time flyout h [Enter].

COMPOUND DENOMINATE MEASURES

Express 1 hr 12 min 10 s as seconds.

(1 hr = 3,600 s, 12 min = 720 s, 10 s - Total 4,330 s)

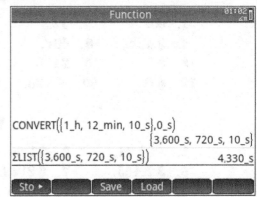

To get the ΣList() command, used in the next screen, press [Toolbox], if necessary soft key [Catlg], scroll the "L's" to select, press soft key [OK].

[Home] Use abbreviated CONVERT as explained in top right screen substituting our new parameters. Get the ΣList() command. Copy list. Press [Enter].

Optional check is to use the <u>Convert units</u> webpage time's drop down to convert one unit to another unit.

NOTE 1. — A **centennial year** is one whose number is divisible by 100. Thus, 400, 1800, and 1900 were centennial years.

NOTE 2. — A centennial year whose number is divisible by 400, or any other year whose number is divisible by 4, is a **leap year**.

Thus, 1600, 1896, and 1904 were leap years.

NOTE 3. — A.M. stands for *forenoon*; P.M. stands for *afternoon*: 7.45 P.M. means 45 *minutes past* 7 P.M.

Exercise 97

1. The winter months are December, January, and February; how many days are there in the winter months?

2. A family that uses 2 qt. of milk a day spends how much for milk during March, the cost of the milk being 6 ¢ a quart?

3. Name the 7th day of the week; the 5th; the 2d; the 1st; the 4th; the 3d; the 6th.

4. Name the months that have 30 days.

5. When a pulse beats 18 times in 15 seconds, how many times does it beat in a minute?

6. A building was erected in MDCCCXC; how many years ago was that?

7. Name the months that have 31 days.

8. One coin is dated 1880, another 1912; how many years are there between their dates?

9. Name the 11th month; the 4th; the 7th; the 12th; the 8th; the 3d; the 6th; the 1st; the 9th; the 2d; the 5th; the 10th.

Page 71

ANSWERS

Exercise 96, page 129

1. $16.83. 2. $11.64. 3. $32.62. 4. $16.56. 5. $32.50.
6. $77.04. 7. $32.25. 8. $2.835. 9. $34.20. 10. $13.77.
11. $29.89. 12. $42.84. 13. $60.25. 14. $43.50.

Exercise 97, page 131

1. 90 ; 91. 2. $3.72. 5. 72. 8. 32. 11. $1.80. 12. $360.
13. $17.50.

Exercise 98, page 133

1. 36 ; 6 ; 18. 2. 9 ; 1½ ; 4½. 3. 16. 4. ½. 5. ⅓.
6. 1½. 7. 58. 8. 68 ft. 9. 36. 11. 480.
12. 9 ; 27. 13. ½. 14. ⅛. 15. 5 ft. 16. 25.

Exercise 99, page 135

8. 3 ; 2. 9. 120 ; 180. 10. 90. 11. A right angle.
12. A right angle. 13. A right angle. 14. 45. 15. 45.

Exercise 101, page 138

3. 4. 4. 16. 5. 25. 6. ¼ ; 36. 7. 10.
8. 1/10. 9. 10. 10. 272½. 11. 4840. 12. 43,560.
13. 160 rd. 14. 600 ft. 15. $6.40. 16. 40. 17. 102,400.
18. 640. 19. 24. 20. 36. 21. 500. 22. 54.

Exercise 102, page 140

1. 10 ft. 2. 56 rd. 3. 140. 4. 1. 5. 360. 6. 13½.
7. 84. 8. 93¼. 9. 4⅓. 10. 1458. 11. 33¼. 12. 78¼.

Exercise 103, page 144

1. 64. 2. 125. 3. 54. 4. 5184. 5. 100.
6. 21⅔. 7. 6. 8. 40. 9. 1620. 10. 180.
14. 55,296. 15. 320. 16. 576. 17. 32. 18. 32.
19. 192. 20. 500 lb. 21. 64.375. 22. 750.

Exercise 104, page 147

1. 120 hr. 2. 480 min. 3. 34 qt. 4. 192 oz.
5. 120 in. 6. 88 yd. 7. 268 oz. 8. 32 pt.
9. 384 qt. 10. 21,600 sec. 11. 132 ft. 12. 54 sq. ft.

Length

Thursday, December 9, 2021   8:48 AM

MEASURES OF LENGTH

Length 12 in = 1 ft 3 ft = 1 yd 5,280 ft = 1 mi What part of a foot is 6 inches? 10 inches? (1/2 ft, 5/6 ft) How many feet are there in 4 miles? 8 miles? 30 miles? (21,120 ft, 42,240 ft, 158,400 ft)	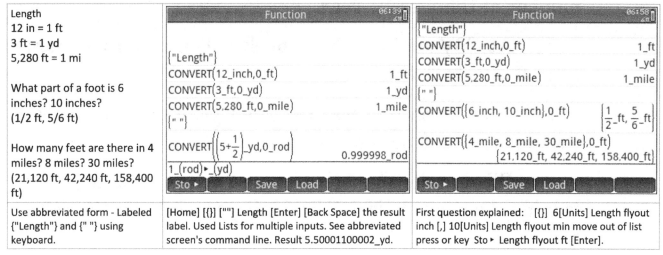	
Use abbreviated form - Labeled {"Length"} and {" "} using keyboard.	[Home] [{}] [""] Length [Enter] [Back Space] the result label. Used Lists for multiple inputs. See abbreviated screen's command line. Result 5.50001100002_yd.	First question explained: [{}] 6[Units] Length flyout inch [,] 10[Units] Length flyout min move out of list press or key Sto ▶ Length flyout ft [Enter].

COMPOUND DENOMINATE MEASURES

Express 1 m 12 cm 10 mm as millimeters.

(1 m = 1,000 mm, 12 cm = 120 mm, 10 mm - Total 1,130 mm)

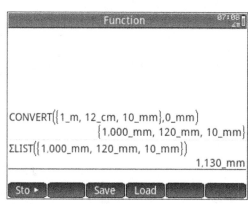

To get the ΣList() command, used in the next screen, press [Toolbox], if necessary soft key [Catlg], scroll the "L's" to select, press soft key [OK].

[Home] Use abbreviated CONVERT as explained in top right screen substituting our new parameters. Get the ΣList() command. Copy list. Press [Enter].

Optional check is to use the Convert units webpage length's drop down to convert one unit to another unit.

132   DENOMINATE AMOUNTS

10. Name the Roman letters that are used to write the number of the present year.

11. At 20 ¢ an hour, how much will a motorman earn from 6 A.M. to 3 P.M.?

12. How much rent was paid in 1 yr. 6 mo. for a house that rented for $ 20 a month?

13. When a hotel is charging 50 ¢ a meal and $1 for lodging, how much is it charging per week at the same rate?

MEASURES OF LENGTH

122. The standard unit of length is the **yard.**

Table

12 inches (in.)	= 1 foot (ft.)
3 feet	= 1 yard (yd.)
$5\frac{1}{2}$ yards	= 1 rod (rd.)
320 rods	= 1 statute mile (mi.)

123.   **Other Measures of Length**

A **fathom** = 6 ft., used to measure the depth of the sea.

A **hand** = 4 in., used in measuring a horse's height.

A **geographic mile,** or knot = 6086 ft.

A **league** (England and U. S.) = 3 geographic miles, used to measure distances at sea.

A **chain** = 4 rd., used by surveyors in measuring land.

MEASURES OF LENGTH 133

Exercise 98

1. How many inches are there in 3 ft.? in $\frac{1}{2}$ ft.? in $1\frac{1}{2}$ ft.?

2. How many feet are there in 3 yd.? in $\frac{1}{2}$ yd.? in $1\frac{1}{2}$ yd.?

3. How many 6-in. ropes can be cut from a rope 8 ft. long?

4. A 6-in. rule is what part of a foot long?

5. A 4-in. rule is what part of a foot long?

6. An 18-in. rule is how many feet long?

7. A horse that is $14\frac{1}{2}$ hands high is how many inches high?

8. What is the distance around a room 24 ft. long and 10 ft. wide?

9. A yardstick was marked off in inches; how many inches?

10. 1 rd. $= 5\frac{1}{2} \times 3$ ft., or —— ft.

11. The ocean, at a certain place, is 80 fathoms deep; how many feet is that?

12. How many inches are there in $\frac{1}{4}$ yd.? in $\frac{3}{4}$ yd.?

13. What part of a yard is a foot?

14. What part of a yard is 6 in.?

15. What is the distance around a boy's hoop if it turns 4 times in a distance of 20 ft.?

16. In ordinary walking, the pace is $2\frac{1}{2}$ ft.; how many feet are there in 10 paces?

ANSWERS

Exercise 96, page 129

1. $16.83.   2. $11.64.   3. $32.62.   4. $16.56.   5. $32.50.
6. $77.04.   7. $32.25.   8. $2.835.   9. $34.20.   10. $13.77.
11. $29.89.   12. $42.84.   13. $60.25.   14. $43.50.

Exercise 97, page 131

1. 90 ; 91.   2. $3.72.   5. 72.   8. 32.   11. $1.80.   12. $360.
13. $17.50.

Exercise 98, page 133

1. 36 ; 6 ; 18.   2. 9 ; 1½ ; 4½.   3. 16.   4. ½.   5. ⅓.
6. 1½.   7. 58.   8. 68 ft.   9. 36.   11. 480.
12. 9 ; 27.   13. ½.   14. ⅛.   15. 5 ft.   16. 25.

Exercise 99, page 135

8. 3 ; 2.   9. 120 ; 180.   10. 90.   11. A right angle.
12. A right angle.   13. A right angle.   14. 45.   15. 45.

Exercise 101, page 138

3. 4.   4. 16.   5. 25.   6. ¼ ; 36.   7. 10.
8. 1/16.   9. 10.   10. 272½.   11. 4840.   12. 43,560.
13. 160 rd.   14. 600 ft.   15. $6.40.   16. 40.   17. 102,400.
18. 640.   19. 24.   20. 36.   21. 500.   22. 54.

Exercise 102, page 140

1. 10 ft.   2. 56 rd.   3. 140.   4. 1.   5. 360.   6. 13½.
7. 84.   8. 93¼.   9. 4½.   10. 1458.   11. 33¼.   12. 78¾.

Exercise 103, page 144

1. 64.   2. 125.   3. 54.   4. 5184.   5. 100.
6. 21⅓.   7. 6.   8. 40.   9. 1620.   10. 180.
14. 55,296.   15. 320.   16. 576.   17. 32.   18. 32.
19. 192.   20. 500 lb.   21. 64.375.   22. 750.

Exercise 104, page 147

1. 120 hr.   2. 480 min.   3. 34 qt.   4. 192 oz.
5. 120 in.   6. 88 yd.   7. 268 oz.   8. 32 pt.
9. 384 qt.   10. 21,600 sec.   11. 132 ft.   12. 54 sq. ft.

Surfaces - Area

Thursday, December 9, 2021   8:49 AM

MEASURES OF SURFACE - AREA

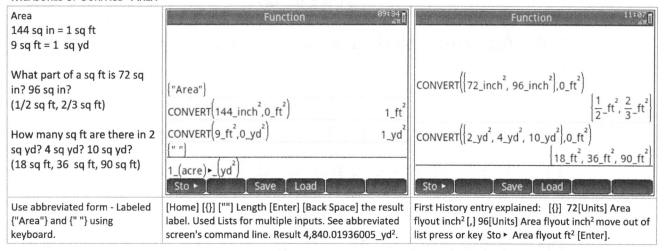

| Area
144 sq in = 1 sq ft
9 sq ft = 1 sq yd

What part of a sq ft is 72 sq in? 96 sq in?
(1/2 sq ft, 2/3 sq ft)

How many sq ft are there in 2 sq yd? 4 sq yd? 10 sq yd?
(18 sq ft, 36 sq ft, 90 sq ft) | $\{"Area"\}$
$CONVERT\left(144\_inch^2,0\_ft^2\right)$ $\qquad 1\_ft^2$
$CONVERT\left(9\_ft^2,0\_yd^2\right)$ $\qquad 1\_yd^2$
$\{"\ "\}$
$1\_(acre)\blacktriangleright\_\left(yd^2\right)$ | $CONVERT\left(\{72\_inch^2,\ 96\_inch^2\},0\_ft^2\right)$
$\qquad\left\{\frac{1}{2}\_ft^2,\ \frac{2}{3}\_ft^2\right\}$
$CONVERT\left(\{2\_yd^2,\ 4\_yd^2,\ 10\_yd^2\},0\_ft^2\right)$
$\qquad\left\{18\_ft^2,\ 36\_ft^2,\ 90\_ft^2\right\}$ |
| Use abbreviated form - Labeled {"Area"} and {" "} using keyboard. | [Home] [{}] [""] Length [Enter] [Back Space] the result label. Used Lists for multiple inputs. See abbreviated screen's command line. Result 4,840.01936005_yd². | First History entry explained: [{}] 72[Units] Area flyout inch² [,] 96[Units] Area flyout inch² move out of list press or key Sto ▸ Area flyout ft² [Enter]. |

People compare the size of the playing area on a football field, 53 1/3 yd by 100 yd, to an acre? What are the sizes of both in square yards? If we subtracted 10 yards from the length would this be a better approximation of an acre? (acre approximately 4,840 yd², playing field approximately 5,333 yd², yes 4,800 yd² is closer)

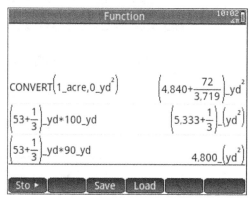

[Home] Use abbreviated CONVERT as explained in top right screen substituting our new parameters for each entry. Press [Enter].

Optional check is to use the <u>Convert units</u> webpage area's drop down to convert one unit to another unit.

SURFACES

130. Anything that has length and breadth without thickness is called **surface**.

131. A surface on which any number of straight lines can be drawn in different directions is a **plane surface**.

132. The *number* of square units in a surface is its **area**.

The Square

133. A **square** is a plane figure that has four equal sides and four right angles.

134. 1. A **square inch** is a square 1 inch long.

2. A **square foot** is a square 1 foot long.

3. A **square yard** is a square 1 yard long.

4. A **square rod** is a square 1 rod long.

5. A **square mile** is a square 1 mile long.

6. A **square unit** is a square 1 unit long.

135. The result obtained by using a number twice as a factor is the **square** of the number.

Thus, 3×3, or 9, is the square of 3.

136. *ABCD* is a square 3 units long.

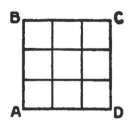

$3 =$ the number of square units in 1 row.
$3 =$ the number of rows of square units.
3×3, or $9 =$ the number of square units in *ABCD*.

Note. — 3×3 may be written 3^2, read *3 squared*.

137. **The area of a square is the square of the number of units in its length.**

138 DENOMINATE AMOUNTS

Exercise 100

1. A square 1 foot long is how many inches long?

2. How many square inches are there in a square 12 in. long?

3. How many feet long is a square a yard long?

4. Represent on the blackboard a square 1 yd. long; scale: $2'' = 1'$. Show how many square feet this square contains.

5. How many square feet are there in a square yard?

6. Represent on the blackboard a square $5\frac{1}{2}$ yd. long; scale: $2'' = 1'$. Show how many square yards this square contains.

7. 1 sq. rd. = —— sq. yd.

138. Table

144 square inches (sq. in.)	= 1 square foot (sq. ft.)
9 square feet	= 1 square yard (sq. yd.)
$30\frac{1}{4}$ square yards	= 1 square rod (sq. rd.)
160 square rods	= 1 acre (A.)

A square rod is also called a **perch**.

Exercise 101

1. Point out three plane surfaces in this room.

2. Point out three surfaces that are not plane.

3. How many square inches are there in a square 2 in. long (a 2-in. square)?

4. How many square inches are there in a 4-in. square?

5. How many square inches are there in a 5-in. square?

6. A square ½ ft. long contains what part of a square foot? How many square inches does it contain?

7. Make a drawing representing a square 40 rd. long; scale: 2″ = 5 rd. How many acres are there in this square?

8. Make a drawing representing a square 4 rd. long; scale: 2″ = 1 rd. What part of an acre does this square contain?

9. How many squares 4 rd. long contain an acre?

10. How many square feet are there in a square rod?

11. How many square yards are there in an acre?

12. How many square feet are there in an acre?

13. What is the distance around (the **perimeter** of) a square 40 rd. long?

14. What is the perimeter in feet of a square lawn 50 yd. long?

15. Find the cost at 40 ¢ per rod of a fence that will inclose a square garden 66 ft. long.

16. How many acres are there in a tract of land in the form of a square 80 rd. long?

17. How many square rods are there in a square mile?

18. Divide the number of square rods in a square mile by 160 to find the number of acres in a square mile?

19. How many square feet of paper will cover a box 2 ft. long, 2 ft. wide, and 2 ft. high?

x   ANSWERS

Exercise 96, page 129

1. $16.83.   2. $11.64.   3. $32.62.   4. $16.56.   5. $32.50.
6. $77.04.   7. $32.25.   8. $2.835.   9. $34.20.   10. $13.77.
11. $29.89.   12. $42.84.   13. $60.25.   14. $43.50.

Exercise 97, page 131

1. 90 ; 91.   2. $3.72.   5. 72.   8. 32.   11. $1.80.   12. $360.
13. $17.50.

Exercise 98, page 133

1. 36 ; 6; 18.   2. 9 ; $1\frac{1}{2}$; $4\frac{1}{2}$.   3. 16.   4. $\frac{1}{2}$.   5. $\frac{1}{3}$.
6. $1\frac{1}{4}$.   7. 58.   8. 68 ft.   9. 36.   11. 480.
12. 9 ; 27.   13. $\frac{1}{2}$.   14. $\frac{1}{8}$.   15. 5 ft.   16. 25.

Exercise 99, page 135

8. 3 ; 2.   9. 120 ; 180.   10. 90.   11. A right angle.
12. A right angle.   13. A right angle.   14. 45.   15. 45.

Exercise 101, page 138

3. 4.   4. 16.   5. 25.   6. $\frac{1}{4}$; 36.   7. 10.
8. $\frac{1}{10}$.   9. 10.   10. $272\frac{1}{4}$.   11. 4840.   12. 43,560.
13. 160 rd.   14. 600 ft.   15. $6.40.   16. 40.   17. 102,400.
18. 640.   19. 24.   20. 36.   21. 500.   22. 54.

Exercise 102, page 140

1. 10 ft.   2. 56 rd.   3. 140.   4. 1.   5. 360.   6. $13\frac{1}{4}$.
7. 84.   8. $93\frac{1}{4}$.   9. $4\frac{1}{3}$.   10. 1458.   11. $33\frac{1}{4}$.   12. $78\frac{1}{4}$.

Exercise 103, page 144

1. 64.   2. 125.   3. 54.   4. 5184.   5. 100.
6. $21\frac{1}{2}$.   7. 6.   8. 40.   9. 1620.   10. 180.
14. 55,296.   15. 320.   16. 576.   17. 32.   18. 32.
19. 192.   20. 500 lb.   21. 64.375.   22. 750.

Exercise 104, page 147

1. 120 hr.   2. 480 min.   3. 34 qt.   4. 192 oz.
5. 120 in.   6. 88 yd.   7. 268 oz.   8. 32 pt.
9. 384 qt.   10. 21,600 sec.   11. 132 ft.   12. 54 sq. ft.

Solids - Volume

Thursday, December 9, 2021   8:49 AM

MEASURES OF SOLIDS - VOLUME

Volume 1,728 cu in = 1 cu ft 27 cu ft = 1 cu yd What part of a cu ft is 720 cu in? 960 cu in? (5/12 cu ft, 5/9 cu ft) How many cu ft are there in 2 cu yd? 4 cu yd? 10 cu yd? (54 cu ft, 108 ft cu, 270 cu ft)	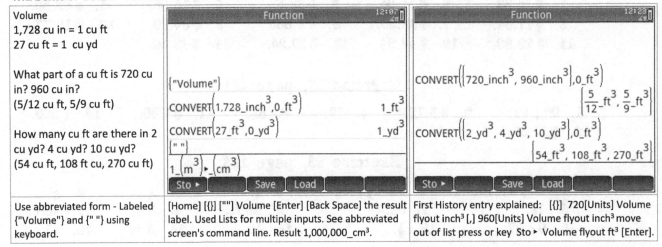	
Use abbreviated form - Labeled {"Volume"} and {" "} using keyboard.	[Home] [{}] [""] Volume [Enter] [Back Space] the result label. Used Lists for multiple inputs. See abbreviated screen's command line. Result 1,000,000_cm³.	First History entry explained: [{}] 720[Units] Volume flyout inch³ [,] 960[Units] Volume flyout inch³ move out of list press or key Sto ▸ Volume flyout ft³ [Enter].

People How many cubic yards are there in a cube 2 1/2 ft long, round to nearest ten-thousandth? (0.5787 cu yd)

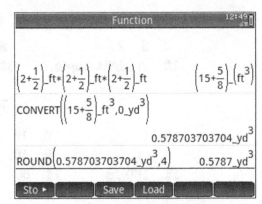

To get the ROUND() command, used in the next screen, press [Toolbox], if necessary soft key [Catlg], scroll the "R's" to select, press soft key [OK].

[Home] Use abbreviated CONVERT as explained in top right screen substituting our new parameters. Get the ROUND() command. Copy number [,] [4]. [Enter].

Optional check is to use the Convert units webpage area's drop down to convert one unit to another unit.

142   DENOMINATE AMOUNTS

146. The **edges** of a cube are the lines in which the squares meet, and the **faces** are the equal squares.

147.

1. A **cubic inch** is a cube an inch long.

2. A **cubic foot** is a cube a foot long.

3. A **cubic yard** is a cube a yard long.

4. A **cubic unit** is a cube a unit long; that is, a cube of any desired length.

NOTE. — The result obtained by using a number three times as a factor is the cube of the number.

Thus, 3 × 3 × 3, or 27, is the cube of 3.

148. This figure represents a cube 3 units long.

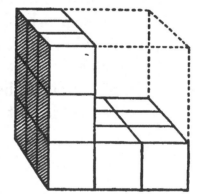

3 = the number of cubic units in one row.

3 = the number of rows.

3 × 3 = the number of cubic units in one layer.

3 = the number of layers.

3 × 3 × 3 = the number of cubic units in the cube.

NOTE. — 3 × 3 × 3 may be written 3³, read *3 cubed*.

149. The number of cubic units in a cube equals the cube of the number of units in the length.

Cubic Measure

150. A cubic foot is a cube 12 in. long.

12 × 12 × 12, or 1728, = the number of cubic inches in 1 cubic foot.

A cubic yard is a cube 3 ft. long.

3 × 3 × 3, or 27, = the number of cubic feet in 1 cubic yard.

144   DENOMINATE AMOUNTS

155.   **Wood Measure**

A pile of wood 8 ft. long, 4 ft. wide, and 4 ft. high is called a **cord**.

Important Facts

A cubic yard of earth is called a **load**.
A cubic foot of water weighs 62½ lb.
A stricken bushel = about $\frac{5}{4}$ of a cubic foot.
A heaped bushel = about $\frac{25}{16}$ of a cubic foot.
A cubic foot of anthracite coal broken averages 54 lb.
400 cubic feet of hay in a mow is considered a ton.
231 cubic inches = 1 wine gallon.
24¾ cubic feet of masonry is called a **perch**.

Exercise 103

1. How many cubic inches are there in a cube 4 in. long?

2. How many cubic feet are there in a cube 5 ft. long?

3. Two cubic yards are how many cubic feet?

4. How many cubic inches are there in 3 cu. ft.?

5. A cubical box 5 ft. long will hold how many bushels of oats, estimating that 1 bu. = 1¼ cu. ft.?

6. How many bushels of wheat will a cubical box hold that is 3 ft. long, estimating that 1 bu. of wheat equals $1\frac{1}{4}$ cu. ft.?

7. How many cubic inches are there in a rectangular solid 3 in. long, 2 in. wide, and 1 in. high?

8. How many cubic feet of sand will a box hold that is 5 ft. long, 4 ft. wide, and 2 ft. high?

9. How many cubic feet of air are there in a room 15 ft. long, 12 ft. wide, and 9 ft. high?

10. How many cubic yards of earth must be removed in digging a cellar 27 ft. long, 18 ft. wide, and 10 ft. deep?

11. Show that there are 128 cu. ft. in a cord.

12. Show that a wall $16\frac{1}{2}$ ft. long, $1\frac{1}{2}$ ft. thick, and 1 ft. high contains $24\frac{3}{4}$ cu. ft., or 1 perch.

13. Show that a vessel 11 in. long, 7 in. wide, and 3 in. deep holds 231 cu. in., or 1 gal.

14. How many gallons of water will a cistern hold that is 28 ft. long, 22 ft. wide, and 12 ft. deep?

SUGGESTION. — $\dfrac{28 \times 12 \times 22 \times 12 \times 12 \times 12}{11 \times 7 \times 3}$ = the number of gallons. (Explain why.)

15. One bushel = about $1\frac{1}{4}$ cu. ft. At this estimate, how many bushels of wheat will a granary hold that is 10 ft. long, 8 ft. wide, and 5 ft. deep?

16. One heaped bushel = about $1\frac{9}{16}$ cu. ft. At this estimate, how many bushels of potatoes will a bin hold that is 15 ft. long, 10 ft. wide, and 6 ft. deep?

ANSWERS

x

Exercise 96, page 129

1. $16.83.   2. $11.64.   3. $32.62.   4. $16.56.   5. $32.50.
6. $77.04.   7. $32.25.   8. $2.835.   9. $34.20.   10. $13.77.
11. $29.89.   12. $42.84.   13. $60.25.   14. $43.50.

Exercise 97, page 131

1. 90 ; 91.   2. $3.72.   5. 72.   8. 32.   11. $1.80.   12. $360.
13. $17.50.

Exercise 98, page 133

1. 36 ; 6; 18.   2. 9 ; 1½ ; 4½.   3. 16.   4. ¼.   5. ⅓.
6. 1¼.   7. 58.   8. 68 ft.   9. 36.   11. 480.
12. 9 ; 27.   13. ⅓.   14. ¼.   15. 5 ft.   16. 25.

Exercise 99, page 135

8. 3 ; 2.   9. 120 ; 180.   10. 90.   11. A right angle.
12. A right angle.   13. A right angle.   14. 45.   15. 45.

Exercise 101, page 138

3. 4.   4. 16.   5. 25.   6. ¼ ; 36.   7. 10.
8. $\frac{1}{10}$.   9. 10.   10. 272½.   11. 4840.   12. 43,560.
13. 160 rd.   14. 600 ft.   15. $6.40.   16. 40.   17. 102,400.
18. 640.   19. 24.   20. 36.   21. 500.   22. 54.

Exercise 102, page 140

1. 10 ft.   2. 56 rd.   3. 140.   4. 1.   5. 360.   6. 13½.
7. 84.   8. 93¼.   9. 4½.   10. 1458.   11. 33¼.   12. 78¼.

Exercise 103, page 144

1. 64.   2. 125.   3. 54.   4. 5184.   5. 100.
6. 21½.   7. 6.   8. 40.   9. 1620.   10. 180.
14. 55,296.   15. 320.   16. 576.   17. 32.   18. 32.
19. 192.   20. 500 lb.   21. 64.375.   22. 750.

Exercise 104, page 147

1. 120 hr.   2. 480 min.   3. 34 qt.   4. 192 oz.
5. 120 in.   6. 88 yd.   7. 268 oz.   8. 32 pt.
9. 384 qt.   10. 21,600 sec.   11. 132 ft.   12. 54 sq. ft.

5

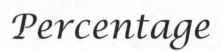

Percentage

"Do not worry about your difficulties in mathematics. I can assure you mine are still greater."
~ Albert Einstein

Definitions and Introductory Exercises

Percent Applications – Using Proportions

Definitions and Introductory Exercises

Wednesday, December 8, 2021   11:52 PM

Definitions

The number or amount of which a given percent is taken is called the **base**.	**Percent** means *hundredths*.
The number of hundredths of the base taken is called the **rate percent**, or the **rate**.	Thus, 1 percent of a number is 0.01 , or $\frac{1}{100}$, of it.
	10 percent of a number is 0.10, or $\frac{10}{100}$, or $\frac{1}{10}$, of it.
	50 percent of a number is 0.50, or $\frac{50}{100}$, or $\frac{1}{2}$, of it.
The result obtained by taking a given per cent of the base is called the **percentage**.	100 percent of a number is 1.0, or $\frac{100}{100}$, or once, of it.
	200 percent of a number is 2.0, or $\frac{200}{100}$, or twice, of it.
FORMULA	The sign *%* stands for percent.
base x rate = percentage	Thus, *6 percent of 25* may be expressed *6 % of 25*.

Type I, II, and III problems - Solve (CAS) and Ratio Proportional (next section) Methods

Finding the Number or Amount (percentage)

1 % of 200 is what number?

$$\frac{1}{100} = \frac{x}{200}$$

Finding a Number When a Certain Percent of it is Given (base)

2 is 25 % of what number?

$$\frac{25}{100} = \frac{2}{x}$$

Finding What Percent One Number is of Another (rate)

8 is what percent of 20?

$$\frac{x}{100} = \frac{8}{20}$$

```
CAS                  Function              10:19

solve(0.01*200=x)                          {2.}
200
---                                          2
100
solve(2=0.25*x)                            {8.}
200
---                                          8
25
solve(8= x/100 *20)
                                           {40}
800
20
Sto ▶  simplify
```

[Home] [Toolbox] [CAS] [3Solve] [1Solve]. Type rest of screen as shown above.

Screen ratios use Proportion Rule - product of means equals product of extremes $\frac{a}{b} = \frac{c}{d}$ i.e. b x c = a x d

61. Memorize this **table of equivalents**

$\frac{1}{2} = 50\%$	$\frac{1}{5} = 20\%$	$\frac{1}{8} = 12\frac{1}{2}\%$	$\frac{1}{3} = 33\frac{1}{3}\%$
$\frac{1}{4} = 25\%$	$\frac{2}{5} = 40\%$	$\frac{3}{8} = 37\frac{1}{2}\%$	$\frac{2}{3} = 66\frac{2}{3}\%$
$\frac{3}{4} = 75\%$	$\frac{3}{5} = 60\%$	$\frac{5}{8} = 62\frac{1}{2}\%$	$\frac{1}{6} = 16\frac{2}{3}\%$
$\frac{1}{20} = 5\%$	$\frac{4}{5} = 80\%$	$\frac{7}{8} = 87\frac{1}{2}\%$	$\frac{1}{12} = 8\frac{1}{3}\%$

62. The number of which a given per cent is taken is called the **base**. The number of hundredths of the base taken is called the **rate**, and the result obtained by taking a given per cent of the base is called the **percentage**.

FINDING PER CENTS

63. Find 5% of 80:

Thus, 5% of $80 = \frac{5}{100}$, or $\frac{1}{20}$, of 80, or **4.**

Exercise 48

In Examples 1–21 find:

1. 1% of 200
2. 50% of 12
3. 25% of 8
4. 20% of 35
5. 10% of 70
6. 5% of 80
7. 2% of 150
8. 4% of 100
9. 40% of 15
10. 60% of 50
11. 30% of 30
12. 90% of 90
13. 75% of 24
14. 8% of 50
15. 25% of \$16
16. $12\frac{1}{2}\%$ of \$0.40
17. 4% of \$200
18. 2% of \$1000
19. 100% of \$2
20. 200% of \$1.50
21. 300% of \$3

250   PERCENTAGE

24. Milk yields butter to the extent of about 4 % of its weight; how much butter will 175 lb. of milk yield?

25. 10 % of all silver coin is copper; find the weight of the copper in silver coin to the weight of 33 lb.

26. If a farmer had 376 bu. of oats, and sold $87\frac{1}{2}$ % of it, how much did he sell?

FINDING A NUMBER WHEN A CERTAIN PER CENT OF IT IS GIVEN

65. 2 is 25 % of what number?

$$2 = \tfrac{25}{100}, \text{ or } \tfrac{1}{4}, \text{ of the required number.}$$
$$\therefore \tfrac{1}{4} \text{ of the required number} = 4 \times 2, \text{ or } 8.$$

Exercise 50

In Examples 1–15 find the number of which:

1. 6 is 50 %	2. 8 is 25 %	3. 3 is 20 %
4. $2\frac{1}{2}$ is 10 %	5. 5 is 1 %	6. 14 is 200 %
7. 4 is 80 %	8. 20 is 400 %	9. 18 is 60 %
10. 36 is 90 %	11. 10 is $12\frac{1}{2}$ %	12. 15 is 75 %
13. 1.5 is 50 %	14. $\frac{3}{5}$ is 60 %	15. 8 is $33\frac{1}{3}$ %

16. $18 is 20 per cent of what sum?

17. $20 is 80 per cent of what sum?

18. 2 yards is 50 % of what length?

19. 2 pounds is 5 % of what weight?

20. $\frac{1}{2}$ ¢ is 50 % of what sum?

21. 50 ¢ is 200 % of what sum?

22. 6 feet is 300 % of what length?

23. 25 lb. is 200 % of what weight?

25. A farmer sold 437.5 bu. of wheat, which was $87\frac{1}{2}\%$ of his wheat crop; find his wheat crop.

SUGGESTION.—$87\frac{1}{2}\%$ of his crop = .875 × his crop.

26. A clerk's expenses were $540, which was $62\frac{1}{2}\%$ of his earnings; what were his earnings?

FINDING WHAT PER CENT ONE NUMBER IS OF ANOTHER

67. 8 is what per cent of 20?

$$8 = \tfrac{8}{20}, \text{ or } \tfrac{2}{5}, \text{ of } 20.$$
$$\therefore 8 = \tfrac{2}{5} \text{ of } 100\% \text{ of } 20, \text{ or } 40\% \text{ of } 20.$$

Exercise 52

In Examples 1–15 state what per cent:

1. 2 is of 4   2. 3 is of 5   3. 1 is of 10

4. 25 is of 75   5. 2 is of 50   6. 5 is of 100

7. 6 is of 30   8. 5 is of 200   9. 4 is of 2

10. 9 is of 9   11. 40 is of 50   12. 60 is of 80

13. $\frac{1}{2}$ is of 1   14. $2\frac{1}{2}$ is of 5   15. $\frac{1}{4}$ is of $\frac{1}{2}$

16. 1¢ is what per cent of 2¢?

17. 2¢ is what per cent of 5¢?

18. 1 quart is what per cent of a gallon?

19. 1 peck is what per cent of a bushel?

20. 1 quart is what per cent of a peck?

21. 1 cent is what per cent of a dime?

22. A quarter dollar is what per cent of a dollar?

23. 2 × any number is how many per cent of it?

ANSWERS

Exercise 48, page 247

1. 2.	2. 6.	3. 2.	4. 7.	5. 7.	6. 4.
7. 3.	8. 4.	9. 6.	10. 30.	11. 9.	12. 81.
13. 18.	14. 4.	15. $4.	16. $0.05.	17. $8.	18. $20.
19. $2.	20. $3.	21. $9.	22. $4.	23. 2¢.	24. 40 bu.
25. 2.	26. 1.	27. 2.	28. 9.	29. $12.	30. 16.
31. 40.	32. 30.	33. $240.	34. 60.	35. $8.	

Exercise 49, page 249

1. 71.5.	2. 100.8.	3. 259.7.	4. 340.2.	5. 419.92.
6. 284.8.	7. 357.28.	8. 206.7.	9. 465.92.	10. 642.
11. 2.	12. $9.	13. $3\frac{1}{4}$ A.	14. $1\frac{1}{4}$ yd.	15. 1760 ft.
16. 800 lb.	17. 19.2 ft.	18. 200 sheep.	19. $600.	20. $2625.
22. $55.	23. $220.	24. 7 lb.	25. 3.3 lb.	26. 329 bu.

Exercise 50, page 250

1. 12.	2. 32.	3. 15.	4. 25.	5. 500.	6. 7.
7. 5.	8. 5.	9. 30.	10. 40.	11. 80.	12. 20.
13. 3.	14. 1.	15. 24.	16. $90.	17. $25.	18. 4 yd.
19. 40 lb.	20. 1¢.	21. 25¢.	22. 2 ft.	23. $12\frac{1}{2}$ lb.	24. 25.
25. $160.	26. $66\frac{2}{3}$ A.	27. 100.	28. $160.	29. 32.	

Exercise 51, page 251

1. 500.	2. 192.	3. 360.	4. 200.	5. $181\frac{1}{3}$.
6. 500.	7. 544.	8. 400.	9. 24000.	10. 448.
11. 96.	12. $76\frac{4}{5}$.	13. $137\frac{1}{2}$.	14. 144.	15. 84.
16. 510.	17. 1920.	18. 248.	20. $480.	21. 3750.
22. 240 rd.	23. 400 ; 260.	24. 400.	25. 500 bu.	26. $864.

Exercise 52, page 253

1. 50%.	2. 60%.	3. 10%.	4. $33\frac{1}{3}$%.	5. 4%.	6. 5%.
7. 20%.	8. $2\frac{1}{2}$%.	9. 200%.	10. 100%.	11. 80%.	12. 75%
13. 50%.	14. 50%.	15. 50%.	16. 50%.	17. 40%.	18. 25%.
19. 25%.	20. $12\frac{1}{2}$%.	21. 10%.	22. 25%.	23. 200%.	24. 300%
25. 500%.	26. 250%.	27. 200%.	28. 400%.	29. 200%.	30. 250%
31. 20%.	32. 80%.	33. 75%.			

Percent Applications - Using Proportions

Wednesday, December 8, 2021   11:54 PM

Equivalent Direct Proportion (see next section Proportion Applications method) - Exercises Screen Results

Relation - Translation equation from word problem. Fill in chart elements.

Relation						
	Original		**Change**		**Result**	
Amount	a *unit*	±	b *unit*	=	c *unit*	
Rate	a %	±	b %	=	c %	

Example: a *unit* : c *unit* = a % : c %   (direct ratio)

a *unit* : c *unit* = a % : c % equivalent to a *unit*: a % = c *unit* : c %

GENERALIZED EQUIVALENT FORMULA

a *unit* : a % = b *unit* : b % = c *unit* : c %

$$\frac{a\ unit}{a\ \%} = \frac{b\ unit}{b\ \%} = \frac{c\ unit}{c\ \%}$$

[Screen: Function 11:31]

$$\frac{100*40}{125} \qquad 32$$

$$\frac{10.5*\left(66+\frac{2}{3}\right)}{100} \qquad 7$$

$$10.5-7 \qquad 3.5$$

$$\frac{100*12}{30} \qquad 40$$

Sto ►   Save   Load

[Home] enter as shown. Need parenthesis ()s for numerator before we press [÷]. Also need parenthesis ()s before selecting mixed numeral template.

Exercises (details first and last problems) - Prime (see above screen - screen results continue below)

Coffee was sold at 40 cents a pound, which was at a profit of 25 % ; find the cost if profit is based on cost. (32)

Cost + Profit = Selling price
x + Profit = 40 cents
100% + 25% = 125%

x:100=40:125

$$\frac{x}{100} = \frac{40}{125}$$

Find the selling price and the loss: If the cost is $10.50, and the rate of loss, 33 1/3%. ($7, $3.50)   10.50:100=selling price:66 2/3 cost-selling price=loss

Serge suit marked down from $30 to $18. What is the rate percent of mark down? (40%) 30:100=12:rate percent

On a bill of goods amounting to $410.20 a discount of 5 % was allowed. Find the cost. ($389.69)   410.20:100=cost:95

When an investment of $65.75 earns $4.50 what is the rate percent of earning, correct to the nearest .01% ? (6.84%)   65.75:100=4.50:rate percent

What principal will amount to $ 595.20 in 2 years 200 day at 4 % ? - assumes a 360 day year, 12 months 30 days each ($55.20, $540)

I=PRT, x=y × 4% × 2 5/9
P + I = A, y + x = 595.20

[Screen: Function 11:56]

$$\frac{410.2*95}{100} \qquad 389.69$$

$$\frac{4.5*100}{65.75} \qquad 6.84410646388$$

$$\frac{200}{360} \qquad \frac{5}{9}$$

$$solve\left(\left\{x=y*0.04*\left(2+\frac{5}{9}\right),\ y+x=595.2\right\},\{x,\ y\}\right)$$
$$\{[55.2\ \ 540.]\}$$

Sto ► simplify

[CAS] first three results, enter as shown. Need parenthesis ()s for first two entries' numerator before we press [÷].

Notice we are using CAS View as solve command is only available in CAS View.

Final problems details: [200] [÷] [360] ;Enter]
[Toolbox] if necessary [Catlg] [9] s key scroll until you find all lower case solve soft key [OK] [{}] enter fist equation [,] enter second equation move out side the list [{}] [x] [,] [y] [Enter].

Read list {[matrix 2 element answer]} as interest Of $55.20 and principal of $540.

COMMERCIAL DISCOUNT 257

70. 1. Find the net cost of a bill of goods amounting to $210 and sold at a discount of 15%.

$210 = the amount of the bill.
.15
———
1050
210
———
$31.50 = the discount.

∴ $210 — $31.50, or $178.50 = the net cost of the bill.

2. What must be paid for a safe listed at $200 and bought at 25% and 10% off?

25%, or ¼, of $200, or $50 = the first discount.
∴ $200 — $50, or $150 = the first remainder.
10% of $150, or $15 = the second discount.
And, $150 — $15, or $135 = the cost.

Exercise 55

1. Find the net cost of a bill of goods amounting to $260 on which there was a discount of 5% allowed.

2. What was the net cost of a rug marked $26 and sold at a discount of 16%?

3. What was the net cost of a bill of hardware amounting to $175 and bought at a discount of 20%?

4. What was the net cost of a bill of furniture amounting to $160 and bought at a discount of 25% and 20%?

5. What was the net cost of an automobile listed at $1600 and sold at a discount of 25% and 20%?

6. What was the net cost of a piano listed at $800 and sold at a discount of 25% and 33⅓%?

260 PERCENTAGE

2. Find the selling price of an article that cost $144 if it was sold at a profit of 12½%.

$144 = the cost.
12½%, or ⅛, of the cost = the gain.
∴ ⅛ of $144, or $18 = the gain;
and, $144 + $18, or $162 = the selling price.

Exercise 57

1. Find the selling price of a machine that cost $150 if it was sold at a profit of 35%.

2. Find the selling price of a horse that cost $150 if it was sold at a loss of 32%.

3. Find the selling price of a wagon that cost $145 if it was sold at a profit of 28%.

4. Find the selling price of a quantity of coal bought for $275 and sold at a profit of 37½%.

5. Find the selling price of a house and lot that cost $3750 and were sold at a profit of 12½%.

Find the gain and selling price if the cost is:

6. $500, and the rate of gain 28%.

7. $488, and the rate of gain 12½%.

8. $630, and the rate of gain 66⅔%.

9. $1000, and the rate of gain 100%.

10. $275, and the rate of gain 1%.

11. $286, and the rate of gain 10%.

Exercise 59

Find the gain or loss per cent:

1. If the cost is $250 and the gain is $50.
2. If the cost is $160 and the gain is $19.20.
3. If the cost is $150 and the gain is $22.50.
4. If the cost is $565 and the loss is $113.
5. If the cost is $200 and the selling price is $250.
6. If the cost is $400 and the selling price is $450.
7. If the cost is $500 and the selling price is $440.
8. If the cost is $800 and the selling price is $775.
9. If an article is bought for $180 and sold for $120.
10. If an article is bought for $250 and sold for $275.

COMMISSION

Definitions

74. Commission is the sum charged by one person for transacting business for another. It is a certain per cent of the money involved in the transaction.

75. When a **sale** is made, *commission is reckoned on the amount of sales ;* when a **purchase** is made, *commission is reckoned on the amount of the purchase.*

Thus, if an agent sells goods to the amount of $300 on a commission of 4 %, his commission is 4 % of $300, or $12. If an agent purchases goods to the amount of $200 on a commission of 2 %, his commission is 2 % of $200, or $4.

76. The **net proceeds** is the sum left after the commission and other expenses have been paid.

xx   ANSWERS

Exercise 53, page 254

1. 25%.   2. 40%.   3. 5%.   4. 8%.   5. 12¼%.   6. 14%
7. 12½%.   8. 33⅓%   9. 33⅓%.   10. 37½%.   11. 125%.   12. 2%.
13. 20%.   14. 3%.   15. 66⅔%.   16. 1%.   18. 25%.   19. 5.4%
20. 5%.   21. 12½%.

Exercise 55, page 257

1. $247.   2. $21.84.   3. $140.   4. $96.   5. $960.
6. $400.   7. $382.50.   8. $206.25. 9. $367.50.   10. $224.
11. $243.

Exercise 56, page 258

11. $2.50.   12. 36¢.   13. 60¢.   14. $3000.   15. 8¢.   16. 28¢.
17. 4¢.   18. $90.   19. 2¢.   20. 12¢.

Exercise 57, page 260

1. $202.50.   2. $102.   3. $185.60.
4. $378.125.   5. $4218.75.   6. $140; $640.
7. $61; $549.   8. $420; $1050.   9. $1000; $2000.
10. $2.75; $277.75.   11. $28.60; $314.60.   12. $208; $442.
13. $115; $345.   14. $272.80; $223.20. 15. $74; $148.
16. $5; $495.   17. $500; $500.

Exercise 59, page 263

1. 20%   2. 12%.   3. 15%.   4. 20%.   5. 25% gain.
6. 12½% gain. 7. 12% loss.   8. 3⅛% loss.   9. 33⅓% loss.   10. 10% gain.

Exercise 61, page 265

1. $268.80.   2. $338.40.   3. $2137.50.   4. $240.25.   5. $10.72.
6. $252.50.   7. $366.075.   8. $467.50.   9. $396.79.   10. $2039.52.
11. $437.15.   12. $96.80.

Exercise 62, page 267

1. $6.   2. $10.   3. $48.   4. $54.   5. $10.   6. $75.   7. $5.
8. $40.   9. $48.   10. $3.

6

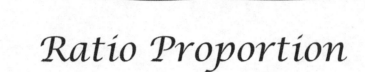

Ratio Proportion

"When the school subjects are
arranged on the basis of the
degree to which they contribute
to the moral upbuilding of
human character good
arithmetic will be well up the
list."
~ George W. Myers

Definitions and Percent Problems by Ratio and Proportion

Ratio Applications

Proportion Applications

Definitions - Percent Problems by Ratio and Proportion

Thursday, December 9, 2021   9:00 AM

Definitions

The **ratio** of one number or amount to another is the result obtained by finding how many times the first, called the **antecedent**, contains the second, called the **consequent**, as a measure.
 	
The **sign** of ratio is the colon (:).
 	
An expression of equality between two equal ratios is called a **proportion**.
    Thus, 2 : 3 = 6 : 9 is a proportion, and may be read, the ratio of 2 to 3 equals the ratio of 6 to 9.
 	
A proportion has four terms ; the first and fourth are called the **extremes**, the second and third the **means**.
	The proportion 10 : 15 = 2 : 3 may be written $\frac{10}{15} = \frac{2}{3}$.
	
	The ratio of two similar amounts may equal the ratio of two other similar amounts ; and the two ratios together form a proportion.
	    Thus, 12 yd : 3 yd = \$8 : \$2 , since each ratio is 4 and may be written 12 : 3 = 8 : 2. This proportion is called a **numerical proportion** ; that is, a proportion whose terms are all numbers.
	
	FORMULA
	In any numerical proportion the product of the means equals the product of extremes.

Ratio and Proportion [$base \; x \; rate \; = \; percentage \; (rate = \frac{percentage}{base})$] rate - a percent that is number of hundredths.

Finding the Number or Amount (percentage)
1 % of 200 is what number? i.e. rate of base is percentage
$$\frac{1}{100} = \frac{x}{200} \qquad 100x = 200$$

Finding a Number When a Certain Percent of it is Given (base)
2 is 25 % of what number? i.e. percentage is rate of base
$$\frac{25}{100} = \frac{2}{x} \qquad 25x = 200 \text{ using the symetric property}$$

Finding What Percent One Number is of Another (rate)
8 is what percent of 20? I.e. percentage is rate of base
$$\frac{x}{100} = \frac{8}{20} \qquad 20x = 800 \text{ using the symetric property}$$

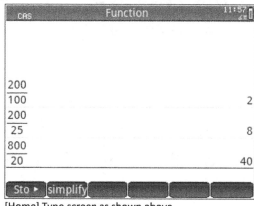

[Home] Type screen as shown above.

410.
$$\text{From } 8:12=2:3$$
$$\text{we have } 8\times 3=2\times 12;$$
$$\text{also, } 8=\frac{2\times 12}{3}, \text{ and } 2=\frac{8\times 3}{12}; \text{ therefore:}$$

1. In a numerical proportion one extreme equals the product of the means divided by the other extreme.

2. In a numerical proportion one mean equals the product of the extremes divided by the other mean.

Exercise 135

In these examples x stands for the missing term; find the value of x:

1. $x:8=4:16$
2. $9:x=12:8$
3. $32:16=x:2$
4. $20:25=100:x$
5. $x:\frac{1}{2}=6:12$
6. $\frac{3}{4}:x=2:\frac{2}{3}$
7. $x:3\frac{1}{3}=10\frac{1}{2}:15$
8. $37\frac{1}{2}:62\frac{1}{2}=5:x$
9. $\$x:\$5\frac{1}{2}=\$12:\$18$
10. $10\text{ yd.}:3\frac{1}{3}\text{ yd.}=x:2$
11. $\$x:\$87\frac{1}{2}=6\text{ yd.}:7\text{ yd.}$
12. $1\text{ bu.}:2\frac{1}{2}\text{ bu.}=\$x:\$10$

Types of Proportion Problems Considered

411. First Type. If 6 lb. of sugar cost 30¢, 12 lb. at the same rate would cost 60¢.

The statement may be abridged thus:

Weight	Cost
6 lb.	30¢
12 lb.	60¢

Ratio Applications

Saturday, December 25, 2021   11:59 AM

Ratio

The expression 12 yd : 3 yd	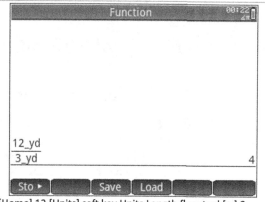
Thus, expression is the number of times that 12 yd contains 3 yd as a measure is to be found. 12 yd is the antecedent and 3 yd is the consequent. The expression is read, the ratio of 12 yd to 3 yd.	
REMARK. The expression 12 yd : 3 yd is called a ratio, and may also be read 12 yd measured by 3 yd.	
The antecedent and the consequent of a ratio are called its terms.	
a. Finding the ratio is simply finding the quotient in comparative division.	
b. The antecedent corresponds to the dividend and the consequent to the divisor.	
c. If one term of a ratio is an amount, the other must be a similar amount.	[Home] 12 [Units] soft key Units Length flyout yd [÷] 3
d. The ratio is always a number.	[Units] soft key Units Length flyout yd [Enter].

Find the missing antecedent (a), consequent (c), or ratio (r).

A cubic foot of water weighs 62.5 lb and a cubic foot of platinum weighs 1345.625 lb; find , correct to the nearest hundredth, the ratio of the weight of platinum to water.

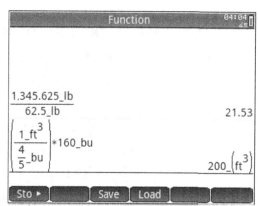

$$a \div b = \frac{a}{b} = r \quad \text{i.e. } 1{,}345.625 \text{ lb} \div 1{,}345.625 \text{ lb} = \frac{1{,}345.625 \text{ lb}}{1{,}345.625 \text{ lb}} = 21.53 = r$$

The ratio of a cubic foot to a stricken bushel is about 4/5. How many cubic feet are there in a bin that holds 160 stricken bushels? (stricken means to level, strike, rather than heap)

$$a \div b = r \quad \text{i.e } x \div 160 \text{ bu} = \frac{1}{\left(\frac{4}{5}\right)} \frac{cu\,ft}{bu}, \quad x = \frac{1}{\left(\frac{4}{5}\right)} \frac{cu\,ft}{bu} * 160 \text{ bu} = 200 \text{ cu ft}$$

[Home] Same technique as above screen.. Be careful with the compound fraction setup and units.

Find the ratio of:

3. $2:5$ 4. $2\frac{1}{2}:5$ 5. $4:3\frac{3}{4}$

6. $3\frac{1}{2}$ yd. $:15$ yd.   7. $\frac{2}{3}$ hr. $:1\frac{1}{4}$ hr.   8. $\$\frac{3}{4}:\$\frac{7}{8}$

Find the missing antecedent (a), consequent (c), or ratio (r):

9. $\dfrac{10}{4}=r$ 10. $\dfrac{a}{4}=12$ 11. $\dfrac{15}{c}=5$ 12. $\dfrac{\frac{3}{4}}{4}=r$

13. $\dfrac{a}{\frac{1}{2}}=2$ 14. $\dfrac{3}{c}=\dfrac{1}{4}$ 15. $\dfrac{\frac{1}{2}}{c}=4$ 16. $\dfrac{a}{5}=.25$

17. In a period of eight years recently, certain food-stuffs advanced in price as given below; state at sight the ratio of the first price to the second:

(1) Tomatoes per can from $8 ¢$ to $12 ¢$.
(2) Peas per can from $10 ¢$ to $12 ¢$.
(3) Corn per can from $6 ¢$ to $10 ¢$.
(4) Apricots per pound from $20 ¢$ to $25 ¢$.
(5) Lamb chops per pound from $20 ¢$ to $28 ¢$.

18. Find the ratio of a short ton to a long ton.

19. A cubic foot of water weighs 62.5 lb. and a cubic foot of platinum weighs 1345.625 lb.; find, correct to the nearest hundredth, the ratio of the weight of platinum to water.

20. The ratio of a cubic foot to a stricken bushel is about $\frac{4}{5}$. How many cubic feet are there in a bin that holds 160 stricken bushels?

Proportion Applications

Sunday, December 26, 2021   8:09 AM

Types of Proportion - Screen solutions for Illustrative Examples

First Type - Directly
If 6 lb of sugar cost $12, 18 lb. at the same rate would cost $36.

Observe:
a. That when the weight is 6 lb., the corresponding cost is $12.
b. That when the weight is 18 lb., the corresponding cost is $36.
c. That 6:18 = 12 : 36.
d. That the ratio of the two values of weight equals the ratio of the corresponding values of cost.
e. If any term of (c) were missing, it could be represented by x and found.

Second Type - Inversely
If 6 lb of sugar can be bought for a certain sum when sugar is $2 per pound, 3 lb can be bought for the same sum when sugar is $4 per pound.

Observe:
a. That when the weight is 6 lb, the corresponding price per pound is $2.
b. That when the weight is 3 lb, the corresponding price per pound is $4.
c. That 6 : 3 = the inverse of 2:4; that is, 6 : 3 = 4 : 2.
d. That the ratio of the two values of weight equals the inverse of the ratio of the corresponding values of the price per pound.
e. If any term of (c) were missing, it could be represented by x and found.

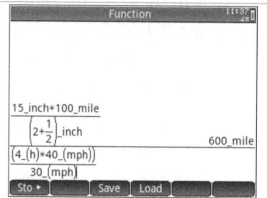

[Home] [()] 15[Units] soft key Units Length flyout inch [x} 100[Units] soft key Units Length flyout mile move right [÷] template 2+1/2[Units] soft key Units Length flyout inch [Enter].

[()] 4[Units] soft key Units Time flyout h [x] 40[Units] soft key Units Speed flyout mph move right [÷] 30[Units] soft key Units Speed flyout mph [Enter]. Result is (5+1/3)_h

Illustrative Examples (product of means equals product of extremes)

When 2 1/2 in on a certain scale represent 100 mi, what distance is represented on the same scale by 15 in? (Direct - 600 mile)

Explanation	
Scale	Distance
$2\frac{1}{2}$ in	100 mi
15 in	x mi

2 1/2 in : 15 in = 100 mi : x mi   (direct ratio)

If a train running 40 miles per hour runs a certain distance in 4 hours, in what time will it run the same distance if it runs 30 miles per hour? (Inverse ratio 30 : 40 to 40 : 30 - 5 1/3 hour)

Explanation	
Time	Rate
x hour	30 mph
4 hour	40 mph

X hr : 4 hr = 40 mph : 30 mph (inverse ratio)

6. When hair for plastering is sold at the rate of $ 0.25 for 7 lb., how much can be bought at the same rate for $ 1.50 ?

7. When 2½ in. on a certain scale represent 100 mi., what distance is represented on the same scale by 15 in. ?

8. It is estimated that 100 lb. of hay possesses the same feeding value as 58 lb. of barley; how much barley has the same feeding value as 1 T. of hay ?

9. If an arc of 30° measures 6 in., what should an arc of 100° on the same circle measure ?

10. If $1.50 will buy a certain quantity of sugar when it sells for $0.05 per pound, what would the same quantity cost when sugar sells at $ 0.08 per pound ?

11. If a train running 40 mi. an hour runs a certain distance in 5 hr., in what time will it run the same distance at the rate of 25 mi. per hour ?

12. A certain sum will buy 100 lb. of sugar at $ 0.05 a pound; what weight will the same sum buy if the sugar is sold for $ 0.06¼ a pound ?

13. An Edison incandescent lamp burning 4 hr. each night will last about 200 nights; how many nights would it last if it were burned 3 hr. each night ?

14. In a plan of a farm 6.25 in. is made to represent a side 1.05 rd. long; what would represent a side 8.4 rd. long?

15. If 40 bu. of grain will last a herd of cows a week when each is fed 4 qt. per day, how long would the same quantity last them, if each were fed 5 qt. per day ?

Made in the USA
Monee, IL
30 July 2024